LOBEY'S THE WEE BOY!

FIVE LOBEY DOSSER ADVENTURES BY BUD NEILL

Compiled by
RANALD MacCOLL

MAINSTREAM
PUBLISHING

EDINBURGH AND LONDON

First published in Great Britain in 1992 by
MAINSTREAM PUBLISHING COMPANY (EDINBURGH) LTD
7 Albany Street
Edinburgh EH1 3UG

ISBN 1 85158 405 6

A catalogue record for this book is available from the British Library

Original cover design by Ranald MacColl

Typeset in 11/14 Optima by David Macdonald Ltd, Edinburgh
Printed in Great Britain by Scotprint Ltd, Musselburgh

CONTENTS

INTRODUCTION

There was an inevitability about Bud Neill's creation of Lobey Dosser.

On Saturdays a young Bud sat in the darkened Troon Playhouse, captivated by Western star William S. Hart's daring exploits on the flickering screen. When he emerged from the matinee gloom to a bright seaside town morning, he harboured secret desires of riding the rolling plains as a cowboy.

Another chunk of his weekend was spent down at the local cabbie's stables where he satiated his other passion, the horse. He would barter some mucking out and grooming for a ride on one of the nags, and for a little while, steely-eyed Hart galloped the roads, greens and beaches of Troon on his faithful steed, Pinto Ben, seeking wrongs to right and heroines to rescue.

Most of us leave childish fantasies behind. Fortunately for us, Bud Neill retained his, and two decades later he spliced them with the stuff of his publicly acclaimed, innovative pocket-cartoons (which tapped the rich resources of Glasgow's *mores* and vernacular) to create the cultural hybrid, Lobey Dosser. The idea had the hallmarks of many brilliant concepts: simple and, with hindsight, obvious.

When the little sheriff rode across page three of Glasgow's *Evening Times* on the 24th of January 1949 his exploits delivered a sharp crack to the city's funny bone and over the next six years the dozen or so adventures acquired an unprecedented following across all social boundaries. The Creek's characters permeated the fabric of city life: in the workplace people were nicknamed Lobey Dosser or Rank Bajin or Toffy Teeth or Rubber Lugs; Lobey became a cult figure among the student body, who made him Honorary President of the Glasgow University Lobey Dosser

Association; fathers became redundant as mothers threatened their unruly offspring with a visit from Rank Bajin; children broke into a street song to the tune of *Ghost Riders in the Sky*. This is one version:

> *My name is Lobey Dosser,*
> *I'm the Sheriff o' Calton Creek.*
> *My steed is El Fideldo*
> *an' it only has two feet.*
> *My enemy is Rank Bajin*
> *an' I'll get him before I die,*
> *an' then I will become a ghost rider in the sky.*

This last accolade, more than any, confirmed Lobey Dosser's place in the city's folklore.

During Bud's earlier visits to the *Evening Times* art department he would amuse a befriended colleague by tagging journalists on the editorial floor with cutting monikers. Later he used this innate talent for inventive namegiving to great effect when he dubbed Calton Creek's characters. This book's players include: Lobey Dosser, an adaptation of lobby dosser — a term applied to tramps who slept on tenement close landings; Dunny Dosser, his brother; Rank Bajin, the villain, ('a creep wi' a black hood an' teeth like a dozen chipped coffee cups'); his wife, Ima Bajin; Fairy Nuff, the tackitty-booted peri who spoke in rhyme; Rid Skwerr, a former foreign spy employed by the town council to haunt their graveyard; Vinegar Hill, a local rabbit farmer, named after a street in Glasgow's East End; Honey Perz, his niece; Whisk E. Glaur, a rancher and his daughter, Adoda; Watts Koakin, the rustler, and the Red Indian contingent, Toffy Teeth and Rubber Lugs. Other tales introduced the characters Stark Stairn, Breedan Mulk, Roona and Nika Boot, Fitz O' Coughin and Khan Oodle.

The G.I. Bride, forever optimistically thumbing her way back to Partick with her baby, little Ned, underarm, was probably a homage to Tommy Morgan's popular stage character, Big Beenie, the G.I. War Bride. Bud was a regular theatergoer in the Forties and admired the energetic originality of Glasgow's home-grown comedians. He must have absorbed the audiences' generous reaction to the comics' parodying and championing of the city's culture and it was no coincidence that the Lobey strips had more than a little flavour of pantomime (the hammy histrionics of Rank Bajin and the rhyming Fairy Nuff, for example). The process turned full circle in the early Fifties when a Lobey skit was included in *Little Red Riding Hood* at the Citizen's Theatre.

When someone once remarked that Bud had a rerr lug for the patter, he could have added that Bud also had a rerr ee for the line. His fluid lines and anchoring blocks of lamp-black ink sat on the paper with such exquisite balance that his cartoons appeared, at times, casually rendered. But a great cartoon strip is more than just superlative draughtsmanship; it is a complimentary partnership of the drawn line and strong, inventive narrative.

Bud exploited the elastic visual and narrative boundaries of the boxed two-dimensional cartoon medium to create a tangible, if quirky, three-dimensional world of well-rounded characters. He was the master and the genie of his lamp-black world and he would unceremoniously dump or manipulate historic, scientific and geographic detail in the interests of a good yarn. Moon rockets, 'single-end' rockets powered by sherbet, plutonium plants, nuclear powered trams, G.P.O. telephones, Sherman tanks, aeroplanes, two-legged horses, pirates, barra-boys and bun-hatted wee wimmen sporting six-shooters all co-existed seamlessly in and around the Caltonesque 1880 frontier Shangri-la known as Calton Creek, Arizona.

I regret not knowing Lobey Dosser. 'Knowing' Lobey in the sense of experiencing him the first time around — fresh from the artist's hand, the creative juices still warm on the page — and participating in the collective eager anticipation of turning the page of the evening paper to catch up on the *real* news of the day at Calton Creek.

The cartoon strip is an ephemeral creature and it is precisely this hit-and-run quality which sorts the wheat from the chaff. Prosaic and glib cartoon art is consigned along with yesterday's newspaper, to the bin and oblivion; the few great strips lodge themselves in the public's psyche. A decade after Lobey's last ride into the sunset Bud was still receiving a steady drip of global correspondence from the little sheriff's *aficionados* offering what amounted to substantial bribes in return for copies of the scarce books reproduced here. And four decades later the Dosser admiration society flourishes — a testament to the enduring popularity of Bud Neill's Indian ink cowboy character.

I hope that this collection of adventures will evoke fond memories in those who enjoyed the strip originally, and I am sure that it will recruit many of the young who through an accident of birth are ignorant of the Creek stories; and that it will finally answer the prayers of the small colonies of the faithful scattered throughout the world.

I leave a last, cosmopolitan word to the Gallic gent who once wandered into the strip and declared: *'Lobey est le petit garçon!'*

* * * * *

The following Lobey Dosser adventures were printed in individual book form some 40 years ago. Over the intervening years the original artwork has been scattered to the four winds, leaving only the newsprint publications to reproduce and I am indebted to Yvonne Barron who assisted me in the restoration of the cartoon strips. I also wish to thank the Neill family, Dougie Baxter and the Evening Times for their co-operation and assistance. Lastly, I thank Bill Campbell and Peter MacKenzie for their saintly patience.

Ranald MacColl
Glasgow, 1992

PROLOGUE

High noon, and in the foothills to the north of Calton Creek a flat-faced squaw is bent over her cooking pots preparing chow for the *Laya Bout tribe.

The old mince and two veg for they're a hungry shower, the Laya Bouts.

Why, the very mention of their name strikes a chill of terror into all but the stoutest hearts, and small wonder! For here are the most savage, ruthless and cunning redskins in the whole West.

From a nearby butte, ominous puffs of smoke rise high. The dreaded war talk of the tribal leader, the fearsome Chief Toffy Teeth.

Blissfully unaware of the fury about to descend upon it, the dusty little township of Calton Creek drowses peacefully in the hot sun. In his office, the redoubtable Sheriff Lobey Dosser is taking time out from his civic duties to fill in his eight draws.

In his burrow at the graveyard, official haunter little Rid Skwerr studies his English grammar, and the dainty Fairy Nuff is busily bashing some sparables into her boots. Suspiciously, the whereabouts of resident villain, Rank Bajin, is at this moment unknown.

All is tranquillity? Don't you believe it, mac . . .

BUD NEILL, 1958

*Originally the Pawnee Tribe

LOBEY DOSSER

By BUD NEILL

HIS LIFE STORY

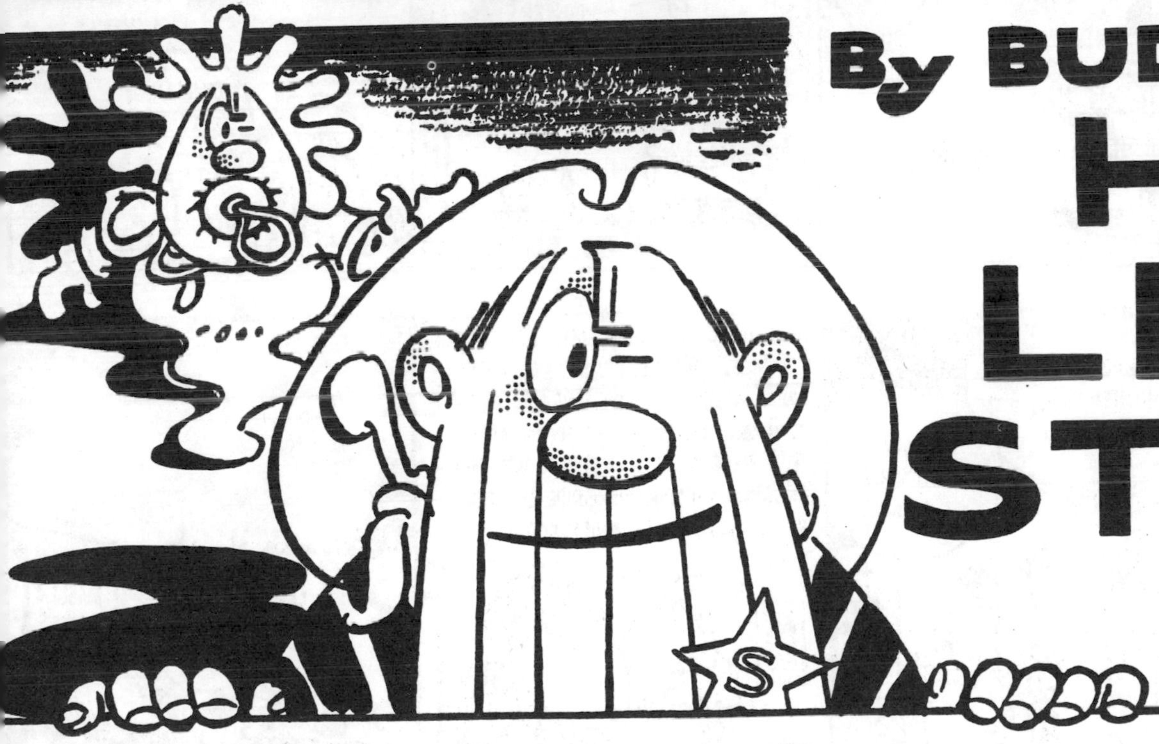

1/-

'SURE ENOUGH, THERE WAS THE MAINLAND AWA' TAE THE EAST - GRIM & FOREBODING, AS THEY SAY IN THE PAPERS...'

AVAST! HERE COMES A BOAT! STAND BY TO SELL YOUR LIVES DEARLY, YE DOGS!

'AS THE BOAT APPROACHED THE ISLAND WE STOOD WAITIN' WI' ONY WEAPONS WE COULD FIND — BITS O' STICK AN' SUCHLIKE ...'

IF ALL ELSE FAILS WE CAN AYE BLIN' THEM WI' SEA-GULLS EGGS, CAPTAIN!

SILENCE, DOG!

TERRIBLE RUDE, THIS BLOKE

'THE FOLK IN THE BOAT SEEMED FRIENDLY AN' STERTED WAVIN' TAE US ... AN' NAE WUNNER.

YOO-HOO! COO-EEEE!

139

'THEY WERE DOON FAE GLESCA' FOR THEIR HOLIDAYS ... WUR BOAT HUD BEEN WRECKED ON THE LADY ISLE, JIST AFF TROON... FELT SUCH A FOOL ...'

WRECKED? AW, THE SHAME! COME ON AN' WE'LL GIE YESE A HURL BACK TAE THE BALLAST BANK... CAN YESE OAR?

LIZZIE

'WE HUNG ABOOT THE TEMPLEHILL IN TROON TILL WE GOT ANITHER BOAT. IT WISNAE LONG ...'

AVAST AND ALL ABOARD! IT'S A STIFF BREEZE AND FULL SAIL FOR THE CARIBBEAN, ME HEARTIES!

'THE NAME O' WUR NEW BOAT WAS THE 'QUEER MARY' BUT LITTLE DID I KEN WHIT WUS IN STORE FOR ME OR I WIDNAE HIV WENT WAN FITT ...'

PEEL ANOTHER SACKFUL OF POTATOES, DOSSER, OR I'LL CLAP YOU IN IRONS! WE ARE APPROACHING THE AZORES!

BEST TATTIES

140

'THE AZORES WERE FAUR AHINT US WHEN A TERRIBLE THING HAPPENED ...'

AVAST! TEAR DOWN THE ENSIGN AND HOIST THE JOLLY ROGER! A FAT MERCHANTMAN APPROACHES!

HIVVENS, THEY'RE PIRATES!

'THROUGH MA WEE TELESCOPE I COULD SEE THE FAT MERCHANTMAN AFF WUR BOW ...'

'ERE YARE NA! RICH SPICES, GOLD, MYRRH, AN' A FEW PAIRS OF NYLONS! AHOY!

HE'S GOING TO GET MYRRH THAN HE BARGAINS FOR...

'EFTER STEALIN' HIS BOATFU' O' STUFF, 'BLACK' SWITE MADE THE FAT MERCHANTMAN WALK THE PLANK...'

TERRIFIC STUFF! HE DID A DOUBLE JACK-KNIFE AND A ONE-AN'-A-HALF SOMERSAULT!

ALMOST AS GOOD AS PETE DESJARDINS, CAP'N!

PLONK!

'THE PIRACY WENT ON EVERY DAY. SOMETIMES THEY WOULD CATCH A WEE THIN MERCHANTMAN INSTEAD O' A BIG FAT WAN...'

ANY USE, CAP?

NO! THROW HIM BACK!

'THEN WAN MORNIN'...'

AVAST! A SPANISH GALLEON APPROACHES LOADED WITH GOLD AND FAIR SENORITAS TO SAY NOTHING OF FOUR QUARTS...

141

FOUR QUARTS, CAP'N?

CERTAINLY, OAF! DOST THOU NOT KNOWEST THAT THERE ARE ALWAYS FOUR QUARTS IN A GALLEON?

SCRATCH SCRATCH

'A TERRIBLE BATTLE TOOK PLACE - CANNON BALLS FLEEIN' ABOOT ALL OWER THE SHOP...'

AVAST! GIVE THEM A BROADSIDE AND TWO NARROW SIDES ... THEY'RE SINKING!

'THE SPANISH GALLEON WAS SOON UNDER THE WAVES ...'

AVAST! WE WON THE BATTLE, BUT OUR SAILS HAVE BEEN SHOT AWAY - ALL EXCEPT THE POOP SAIL, WHATEVER *THAT* IS!

'ABOOT TWO YEAR LATER WE WERE STILL HEADIN' FOR THE CARIBBEAN UNDER WUR WEE POOP SAIL ... AWFY SLOW WORK ...'

LAND HO!

IT'S THE WEST INDIES!

FLYING FISH

142

'I HUD GROWN AN AWFY SIZE SINCE I LEFT GLESCA' ... AN' AS HARD AS NAILS ...'

YO-HO-HOLA, AN' A BOTTLE O' KOLA!

'IN ANITHER FEW MONTHS WE WERE IN THE CARIBBEAN, BECALMED... 'BLACK' SWITE WAS FLAMIN'...'

AVAST! RUN CUT THE YARD-ARM AND BATTEN DOWN THE POOP DECK! WE ARE HOVE-TO, AND IF THERE AIN'T NO WIND BY TONIGHT WE'LL BE HOVE THREE OR MAYBE FOUR! AVAST!

''BLACK' SWITE WAS BILIN'...'

AVAST, DOSSER! GET TO THE STERN AND BLOW ON THE POOP SAIL OR I'LL BELAY YOU WITH MY MARLIN SPIKE! AVAST!

AYE, AYE, CAP'N!

'THAT NIGHT I DECIDED TAE LEAVE THE 'QUEER MARY' TO HER FATE ...'

I'LL TAK' THE WEE DINGHY AN' SCRAM TAE MEXICO AWA' FAE THAE BAD PIRATES ...

BUD NEILL

143

'SO WHILE THE CREW SLEPT...'

'WHEN DAWN BROKE I WUS FAUR AWAY FAE THE 'QUEER MARY' AND THE WICKED PIRATES'...'

I'LL HIV A WEE REST FAE OARIN' NOO, AN' A CUP O' TEA ...

LATER ..

MY, BUT THAT WUS RERR! HO-HI! YAWN. GRUNT. SNORE, SNORE ...

LATER STILL ...

SNORE
SNORE
SNORE
SNORE
SNORE
SNORE
SNORE
SNORE
SNORE
SNORE
SNORE
SNORE

SNORE

144

AND LATER STILL ...

'I WOKE UP TAE FIND A FIERCE BIG CANNIBAL GLOWERIN' AT ME OWER THE SIDE O' THE BOAT ~

A CANNIBAL! IT'S NO' TRUE!

HE CANNIBAL-EVE IT

'HE SHOOK HIS SPEAR AT ME AN' MADE SIGNS FOR ME TAE FOLLOW HIM...'

AYE, OKAY, FIERCE BIG CANNIBAL. I'M COMIN', SO KEEP YIR HAIR ON!

UMPAH!

'I FOLLOWED HIM THROUGH THE JUNGLE FOR 'OORS ...'

UMPAH UMPAH

?

HINT to YOUNG ARTISTS JUNGLES AIN'T EASY...

145

'IT WAS GETTIN' DAURK WHEN WE GOT TAE THE CANNIBAL CAMP ... MY KNEES WAS CHITTERIN' WI' FRIGHT, I CAN TELL YE ...'

WISHT I'D NEVER LEFT MA AUNTIE MABEL ... THE MORN'S NIGHT I'LL BE 'LOBEY FRICASSEE' ON THEIR MENU ... OH, WEEL, I HOPE I'M FU' O' BONES ... SERVE THEM RIGHT ...

'THE CANNIBAL PUT ME IN A MUD HUT AN' LOCKED ME UP WI' TWO ENGLISH MISSIONARIES WHO NATTERED AWAY TO EACH OTHER A' NIGHT...'

TYNT MOOCH OF A MOOD 'OOT, COCK

NOW, TYNT, COCK—WHY BACK IN BRADFORD.. .....

AS IF THINGS WISNAE BAD ENOUGH...

'NEXT MORNIN' THE CANNIBAL STUCK HIS HEID IN THE DOOR AN' CALLED OOT THE TWO MISSIONARIES ...'

HOW RIPPING, CYRIL! I THINK HE'S TAKING US TO BREAKFAST...

NOT '70', YE MUG—'FOR'!

'A WEE WHILE EFTER THE MISSIONARIES HAD WENT THE CANNIBAL CAME BACK WI' A BOWL O' SOUP FOR ME, BUT I WISNAE HUNGRY'

I WUNNER WHICH O' THE TWO THIS IS MADE OOT O', PUIR SOWLS...

146

'THEN ABOOT LUNCH-TIME THE CANNIBAL STUCK HIS LOAF ROON' THE DOOR AGAIN AN' BECKONED ME OOT... I WAS QUAKIN' WI' FRICHT ...'

IT'S NO' RIGHT! A' THAE HARDSHIPS I'VE SUFFERT JIST TAE WIND UP AS A CANNIBAL ENTRÉE ... THIS IS THE FEENISH...

SMACK!

'BUT INSTEED O' PITTIN' ME IN THE STEW-POT, THE CANNIBAL TOOK ME TAE THE BIGGEST MUD-HUT IN THE VILLAGE ...'

THERE'S A LOT O' FOLK HINGIN' ABOOT OOTSIDE ... MUST BE THE LABOUR EXCHANGE ...

'WE GOT TAE THE DOOR AN' THE BIG CANNIBAL PRODDED ME INSIDE WI' HIS SPEAR ... AWFY SORE ...'

OUCH!

'SITTIN' ON A CHAIR SURROUNDED BY HIS COORT WAS THE KING O' THE CANNIBALS ... AN' A WICKED LOOKIN' AULD JOSSER HE WAS TAE ...'

UMPAH, UMPAH!

HE DISNAE WEAR A JUMPAH!

147

'THE MEENIT I SPOKE, BEDLAM BROKE OOT ... EVERYBODY YELLIN' AT WANCE ...'

YELL! YELL! YELL!

?

'WHEN THE YELLIN' DIED DOON THE KING O' THE CANNIBALS MADE EVERYBODY BEAT IT EXCEPT ME ...'

UMPAH, UMPAH!

AYE, THAT'LL BE RIGHT!

'THEN THE CANNIBAL KING SPOKE AGAIN ... YE COULD HIV KNOCKED ME DOON WI' A FEATHER ...'

WHIT PERT O' GLESCA' ARE YE FROM, MAC?

THE CALTON, HOW?

WE'RE FAE CLYDEBANK ... PLEASED TAE MEET YE ...

SO YE'RE NO' REALLY CANNIBALS AT ALL?

NAW

WELL, I NEVER!

WE WERE BLITZED OOT AN' CAME TAE THIS DESERT ISLAND ABOOT SIX YEAR AGO ... BEIN' FAE CLYDEBANK WE SOON CHASED ALL THE CANNIBALS AN' TOOK OWER THE PLACE ON WUR OWN ... WAIT TILL I GET THE WIFE ... SHE'S FAE YOKER ...

YE DON'T SAY! IT'S A SMA' WORLD ...

148

'THE CANNIBAL KING CALLED IN HIS WIFE'

I WANT YE TAE MEET A FREEN' O' MINE'S FAE GLESCA', ANNA ... WHIT'S YIR NAME, MAC ?

DOSSER... LOBEY DOSSER... WHIT'S YOURS?

WUR NAME'S McANNIBAL ... I'M HANNIBAL, AN' THIS IS MY MISSUS, ANNABELLE...

PLEASED TAE MEET YE, MRS McANNIBAL !

HOO DEE DOO!

YOKER PATTER

'EFTER THAT I GOT ON RERR WI' THE TRIBE — BUT I WAS STILL WORRIED ABOOT SOMETHIN' ...'

WHIT HAPPENED TAE THAE TWA ENGLISH MISSIONARIES, HANNIBAL ?

I SENT THEM HAME! WE ONLY DOLLED WURSEL'S UP LIKE CANNIBALS TAE FRICHTEN THE WITS OOT THEM—NO A HARD JOB... C'MON AN' I'LL SHOW YE ROON' THE PLACE...

AYE, OKAY!

149

SMASHIN' WEATHER YE GET HERE, HANNIBAL ... SAUN' AN' EVERYTHIN' ... IF IT WUS NEARER GLESCA' YE'D BE SWAMPED WI' HOLIDAY-MAKERS THE NIGHT... WHIT'S THAT BIG MOUNTAIN OWER THERE ?

THAT'S WHIT THEY CRY THE 'MOUNTAIN O' THE DEID' ... THERE'S SOME QUEER STORIES ABOOT IT TOO ... FOR INSTANCE...

'HANNIBAL TELLT ME ABOOT THE 'MOUNTAIN O' THE DEID'...'

NAEBODY'S NEVER BEEN UP IT... FOLKS HIV TRIED BUT NEVER CAME BACK TAE TELL THE TALE... WAN EXPLORER CAME BACK RAVIN' MAD...

DEAR DEAR DEAR

WELL ... IT'S SAID THAT SOMEWHERE IN THE MOUNTAIN LIVES A TRIBE O' SAVAGES RULED OWER BY A BEAUTIFUL WHITE QUEEN AN' I HOPE I'M NO' PITTIN' ONY IDEAS IN YIR HEID...

NO' ME, NAW !

WELL ... IT'S SAID, TOO, THAT THIS BEAUTIFUL WHITE QUEEN LIVES IN A PALACE O' PURE GOLD AN' EATS RUBIES FOR SWEETIES...

YIR KIDDIN'!

150

AN' BEIN' IN NEED O' SOME DOUGH, I'M LEADIN' AN EXPEDITION INTO THE MOUNTAIN ON MONDAY TAE LOOK FOR THIS TRIBE IF YE'D CARE TAE JYNE US...

AYE, SURE, HANNIBAL—I'LL GO WI' YE ...

'WE WERE SOON PAST THE WICKED SAVAGE & HIS POISONED DERTS—BUT RUNNIN' INTAE MAIR DANGER ...'

MIND YIR HEID ON THE PYTHON, JIMMY!

HAW, ANDY! THERE'S A BIG SCORPION CRAWLIN' UP YIR NECK ...

SO WHUT? I'VE HUD A BLACK WIDDY SPIDER GALLOPIN' ABOOT INSIDE MA SHIRT FOR THE PAST 'OOR ...

'THE FURTHER WE CLIMBED UP THE MOUNTAIN THE WORSE THINGS GOT ...'

A' WUR RATIONS HAS BEEN ETT WI' RID ANTS, HANNIBAL...

AN' WE'VE RUN OOT O' WATTER

HUGHIE'S EYE'S A' SWOLE WI' HIM BEIN' BIT BY A TARANTULA, TAE ...

OCH, COME ON HAME!

WHO SAID 'COME ON HAME'? WE'RE NO' TURNIN' BACK NOO JIST BECAUSE O' A LOT O' FIERCE BEASTS AN' SAVAGES! WE'LL FIN' WATTER AN' SOMETHIN' TAE EAT, SO KEEP YIR PECKERS UP AN' FOLLY ME ...

ATTA BOY!

YE'RE RIGHT!

GUID AULD HANNIBAL!

WE LIVED AFF BERRIES AN' COCONUT MILK FOR DAYS THEN WAN EFTERNOON WE CAME OWER A RIDGE ON THE MOUNTAIN AN' WHIT A SHOCK !

DAE YOU SEE WHIT I SEE ?

IT'S A DINOSAUR — A PREHISTORIC ANIMAL!

THERE'S MEAT RATIONS THERE FOR THE HALE O' GLESCA ...'

'THE BIG DINOSAUR GLOWERED AT US AN' FLAMES CAME OOT ITS NEB ...'

RUN OWER AN' KILL IT, JIMMY!'

AWA' AN' TAKE A JUMP TAE YIRSEL'!

NAE USE STABBIN' IT WI' SPEARS—THEY'D JIST STOAT AFF IT...

I'VE AN IDEA— JIST WAIT HERE A MEENIT!

'I RAN OWER TAE THE BIG DINOSAUR AN' IN A FEW SECONDS IT WAS STONE-CAUL' DEID ...'

LAST

GASP!

WELL, I NEVER!

GREAT STUFF!

LOBEY'S THE WEE BOY!

A LEG FOR ME PLEASE, AN' SOME WHITE MEAT!

WIRE IN!

SEE US A WING IF IT HAS ONY!

HOO DID YE KILL THE BIG DINOSAUR SO QUICK MAY I ASK, LOBEY?

EASY! I JIST SHOWED IT A PICTURE O' ... COUGH, COUGH ... O' A CERTAIN CHANCELLOR O' THE EXCHEQUER SMILIN' ...

Panel 1: 'EFTER WE'D DINED AFF THE BIG DINOSAUR WE PRESSED ON UP THE MOUNTAIN IN SEARCH OF WATTER...'

HOO COULD YE GO A DUMP WI' A BIG DAUD O' ICE IN IT, ANDY?

AW, SHUT UP, YOU!

Panel 2: 'WE CAME TAE A WOODED PERT O' THE COUNTRY AN' SEEN SMOKE RISIN' FAE A WEE HUT...'

TAK' YIR TIME, NOO – IT MIGHT BE A FIERCE SAVAGE'S HOOSE!

THERE A BLOKE WAVIN'!

Panel 3: 'WE WENT OWER TAE THE WEE HOOSE AN' FUN' A QUEER AULD CHAP WAITIN' FOR US...'

GREETINGS AND WELCOME! ALLOW ME TO INTRODUCE MYSELF – I AM THE WORLD RENOWNED NATURALIST, CRAW K. DILE

WHAUR'S YIR WELL, MISTER DILE?

PLEASED TAE MEET YE, MISTER DILE!

155

Panel 4: 'EFTER WE'D DRUNK WUR FILL O' NICE CAULD WATTER, AULD DILE TELLT US ABOOT HIMSEL'...'

I AM STUDYING THE HABITS OF THE PTERODACTYL AND THE PLESIOSAURUS, PREHISTORIC CREATURES WHICH ABOUND IN THESE PARTS ... COME ROUND THE BACK, GENTLEMEN, AND INSPECT MY COLLECTION OF RARE FAUNA, IF YOU PLEASE...

AYE, SURE, MISTER DILE!

Panel 5: CRAW K. DILE SHOWED US ROON' THE PLACE...'

THIS IS THE ONLY GWUMP IN CAPTIVITY —— IT IS PRACTICALLY EXTINCT

IT SURE DOES!

EXTINCT' THE MAN SAID!

Panel 6: BILD NEILL

AND THIS IS A GREATER GOONFILLY, ONE OF THE GIANT MARSUPIALS

ONY PINK ELEPHANTS?

QUIET, YOU!

GOONFILLY FOOD

Panel 7: 'AULD DILE GAVE US WUR TEA AN' THEN WE HUD A WEE CHAT...'

AND WHAT BUSINESS BRINGS YOU GENTLEMEN TO THIS PART OF THE COUNTRY?

WE'RE LOOKIN' FOR THE LOST CITY O' THE MOUNTAIN O' THE DEID WHICH IS RULED OWER BY A BEAUTIFUL WHITE QUEEN, MISTER DILE...

156

Panel 8: WHEN WE TELLT MISTER DILE WHIT WE WERE DAEIN HE GOT AWFY EXCITED'

MY FRIENDS, TAKE WARNING AND DO NOT PROCEED FURTHER! TURN BACK WHILE THERE IS STILL TIME, I BEG OF YOU! THERE ARE STRANGE AND TERRIBLE THINGS IN THE MOUNTAIN WHICH WERE NEVER INTENDED FOR HUMAN EYES TO SEE– DARK & EVIL THINGS! TURN BACK! TURN BACK!

YE GET THAT WAY LIVIN ALANE!

SO YE DO, AYE!

'HANNIBAL McANNIBAL TELLT CRAW K. DILE THAT HE'D NAE INTENTION O' TURNIN' BACK ...'

WE'RE NO' FEART FOR NOTHIN', MISTER DILE. BEIN' FAE CLYDEBANK — NAE AULD SAVAGES IS GOIN' TAE SCARE US ...

WE'RE NO' FEART, NAW!

COME ON, HANNIBAL— LET'S GET WEAVIN'!

'SO EFTER SAYIN' CHEERIO TAE CRAW K DILE WE PUSHED ON UP THE MOUNTAIN ...'

MISTER DILE SAID THERE'S A BIG LAKE ABOOT A DAY'S JOURNEY FAE HERE SO WE'LL NO' HIV TAE GO WI'OOT WATTER ...

I'LL HIV AN OORS PADDLIN' TAE STERT WI', THANK YOU — MA FEETS KILLIN' ME ...

'NEXT MORNIN' WE CAME TO THE BIG LAKE AN' CAMPED FOR THE DAY ...'

SMASHIN', INT IT, CHERLIE — SCRUB MA BACK ...

AWA' AN CHASE YIRSEL'!

HAW, ANDY— HERE'S A WEE JEELY FISH WI' EE'S LIKE RID CURRANTS!

RED CURRANT JELLY FISH

157

'WE WERE A' SPLASHIN' ABOOT IN THE WATTER WHEN A TERRIBLE THING HAPPENED ...'

HIVVENS! A FIERCE BIG OCTOPUS!

RUN FOR YIR LIVES!

MITHER! HELP!

'THE OCTOPUS WAS ABOOT THE SIZE O' THE WEE CUMBRAE WI' FLAMES COMIN' OOT ITS LUGS ...'

WHIT A DIAL!

HORRIBLE, INT IT?

JIST LIKE MA MITHER-IN-LAW ONLY MAIR SOCIABLE LOOKIN'

'WI' A SNORT O' FIRE THE BIG OCTOPUS SLINK UNDER THE WATTER ... GUID JOB, TAE ...'

NAE MAIR PADDLIN' FOR ME, THANKS.

NOR ME!

LET'S PUSH ON, NOO CHAPS!

AYE, COME ON!

'ABOOT A WEEK LATER WE CAME TAE A BIG WATERFALL ...'

NOO WE'RE STUCK! HOO DAE WE GET UP THERE?

SCLIM UP!

DON'T BE DAFT!

THERE'S A CAVE UNDER THE FALL, HANNIBAL!

SO THERE IS, AYE!

158

'LEAVIN' THE MEN TAE MIND THE LUGGAGE, HANNIBAL AN' ME WENT TAE EXPLORE THE FUNNY CAVE ...'

MIND YIR FEET NOO, LOBEY — WAN SLIP AN' YEVE HUD IT!

DAURK, INT IT?

'IT WUS AWFY EERIE INSIDE THE CAVE I CAN TELL YE ... PITCH BLACK TAE ...'

YE A' RIGHT, HANNIBAL?

AYE

WELL HAUD ON A MEENIT TILL I FIN' MA WEE TORCH ... HERE IT IS ...

'WI' THE LIGHT FAE MA WEE TORCH I COULD SEE ROON' ABOOT THE PLACE ...'

IT'S A HUGE BIG CAVE AN' GOES AWA' IN THERE FOR MILES

COME ON AN' WE'LL HIV A SQUINT — MAYBE IT'S FU' O' HIDDEN TREASURE !

'WE'D WENT ABOOT THREE MILE IN TAE THE CAVE WHEN A TERRIBLE THING HAPPENED ...'

GUIDNESS! A FIERCE BIG MAMMOTH BLOCKIN' WUR PATH!

SNARL SNARL

'THEN MA TORCH WENT OOT!'

DASH IT! THAE NUMMER EIGHT BATTERIES!

SNARL

SNARL

SNARL

!

'IN THE DAURKNESS I COULD HEAR THE FIERCE BIG MAMMOTH SNUFFLIN' ABOOT AN' COULD FEEL ITS HOT BREATH ON MA FACE ... IT WAS LOOKIN' FOR US TAE EAT FOR ITS DINNER, D'YE SEE ...'

JIST STAUN' STILL AN' HAUD YIR BREATH, HANNIBAL!

SNUFFLE SNUFFLE SNUFFLE

SNARL SNARL SNARL

'WHEN IT COULDNAE FIN' US THE BIG MAMMOTH LOST ITS RAG AN' FLAMES CAME OOT ITS NEB WI' ANGER ...'

TRY AN' SNEAK PAST IT BY THE LIGHT O' THAE FLAMES, HANNIBAL ... HURRY UP NOO AFORE IT COOLS DOON!

AYE, OKAY!

'WE WERE LUCKY ... THE BEAST DIDNAE SEE US AN' WE'RE SOON PAST IT AN' ON OUR WAY DEEPER INTAE THE CAVE ...'

AWFY SLOW WORK IN THE DAURK, HANNIBAL!

IT IS THAT, AYE ... NO' EVEN A MATCH!

'ABOOT TWO MILE FURTHER ON WE GOT A RIGHT SHOCK ...'

GLIMMER GLIMMER

DAE YOU SEE SOMETHIN' GLIMMERIN' AWA' DOON THERE, HANNIBAL?

AYE, IT'S A LIGHT O' SOME KIND!

THE WEE FOAL FOLLOWED ME ABOOT ALL DAY AN' BY NIGHT-TIME HANNIBAL AN' ME HAD CAME TAE THE EDGE O' THE PLATEAU...'

I'M DEID BATE

WE'LL STOP HERE TILL MORNIN'... LIE DOON AN' HAE A SLEEP, WEE FOAL...

'WE TUCKED WURSEL'S IN WI' NICE WARM GRASS AGAINST THE CAUL' NIGHT AIR AN' WERE SOON FAST ASLEEP...'

SNORE SNORE SNORE

'ABOOT FOWER IN THE MORNIN' I WOKE UP WI' A FUNNY FEELIN' THAT SOMEBODY WAS WATCHIN' US...'

PSSST! HANNIBAL. HIV A LOOK OWER THERE!

SNORE SNORE

'BUT HANNIBAL WAS SOUND ASLEEP — AN' STAUNIN' A FEW YERDS AFF GLOWERIN' AT US WAS A FIERCE WHITE SAVAGE WI' A SPEAR!'

MITHER! WHY DID I LEAVE THE CALTON!

THE FIERCE WHITE SAVAGE WAS JIST ABOOT TAE PLUNGE HIS SPEAR AT US WHEN HE SEEN THE WEE FOAL...'

THANK GUIDNESS YE'VE WOKE, HANNIBAL — LOOK AT THIS FIERCE WHITE SAVAGE!

OH, HEAVENS — LOOK AT THE HERR TAE! HE'S LIKE SOMETHIN' OOT THE ERT SKILL

HEY — WIS YE AT THE ERT SKILL, FIERCE WHITE SAVAGE?

ECTUALLY NO, OLD CHEP...'VARSITY... TOOK MY B.Sc. IN BLACK MEDICINE... DASHED INTERESTED IN YOUR HORSE, OLD MAN... RAWTHER

'THE FUNNY SAVAGE TELLT US ABOOT MA WEE FOAL...'

SACRED BEASTS WITH OUR TRIBE, OLD BOY... ABSOLUTELY UNTAMEABLE ... FIRST I'VE SEEN IN CAPTIVITY... WIZARD SIGHT, OLD MAN... MUST COME AN' MEET THE QUEEN NOW... SHE'LL BE INTRIGUED...

AYE OKAY

'WE FOLLOWED THE EDUCATED SAVAGE AN' AT LAST WE CAME TAE A CITY... WHIT A PLACE TAE!'

WHAUR'S YIR KILBOOIE ROAD NOO, HANNIBAL? A' THAE BUILDINS IS PURE GOLD AN' THE TRAMCAURS IS MADE O' PLATINUM...

THE PALACE IS ONLY A SHORT DISTANCE NOW, OLD BOY...

22 CARAT

'WE SOON GOT TAE THE PALACE AN' WERE SHOWED INTAE THE QUEEN'S ROOM ... WHIT A SHOCK!'

HULLO, QUEEN OLD GAL ... COUPLE OF CHAPS I MET ... HAVE A TAME SACRED FOAL ... AMAZING, WHAT?

HOW INTERESTING!

'THE QUEEN WAS A HUM-DINGER— A WEE HONEY...

DO SIT DOWN AND TELL ME OF HOW YOU CAME TO HAVE THIS TAME FOAL — I'LL RING FOR TEA ...

AWFY NICE O' YE, QUEEN

'OVER WUR NICE TEA (SMASHIN' WEE SODY SCONES AN' EVERYTHIN') WE TELLT THE QUEEN A' ABOOT WUR ADVENTURES ...'

AN' THAT'S HOO WE CAME TAE BE HERE, QUEEN

HOW THRILLING! NOW MISTER McANNIBAL WILL WISH TO RETURN TO HIS BAGGAGE PARTY AT THE MOUTH OF THE CAVE AND THENCE TO HIS VILLAGE... I WILL SEND AN ESCORT WITH HIM TOMORROW... AND YOU, MISTER DOSSER?

QUEEN'S BEST CHEENY

I'D LIKE TAE GO TAE MEXICO, QUEEN — BUT I'D LIKE TAE 'TAK' THE WEE FOAL WI' ME IF THAT'S A' RIGHT

CERTAINLY— THE FOAL IS YOURS, MISTER DOSSER— I SHALL ARRANGE FOR YOUR TRANSPORTATION TO MEXICO IMMEDIATELY— NOW I WILL HAVE A SERVANT SHOW YOU TO YOUR ROOM...

C 1 6 5 BUD NEILL

'EFTER A GUID NIGHT'S SLEEP IN AN 18 CARAT GOLD BED WI' A SILVER PLATED MATTRESS I WAS READY FOR MY FURTHER ADVENTURES'

BREAKFAST IS SERVED, GENTS!

THANKS A LOT, MAC

'EFTER BREAKFAST THE QUEEN SENT FOR US ...'

ALL READY FOR THE ROAD NOW? THEN COME WITH ME ... WE HAVE A PRIVATE CHUTE TO MEXICO, MR DOSSER— AND YOUR ESCORT IS WAITING TO SEE YOU SAFELY HOME, MR McANNIBAL

'THE QUEEN TOOK ME TAE THE CHUTE WI' MA WEE FOAL AN' I SAID CHEERIO TAE HANNIBAL

KEEP THE HEID NOO, HANNIBAL, AN' GUID LUCK TAE YE ... TELL THE WIFE I WAS ASKIN' FOR HER ...

CHUTE TO MEXICO

TA-TA, LOBEY... IT'S BEEN NICE KNOWIN' YE ...

THANKS, QUEEN - YE'VE BEEN AWFY KIND — CHEERIO, THEN ...

BEFORE YOU GO, MR. DOSSER, WOULD YOU ALLOW ME TO CHRISTEN YOUR FOAL?

AYE, SURE, QUEEN

GOOD! THEN I CHRISTEN HER EL FIDELDO' WHICH IS NEILL SPANISH FOR 'THE FAITHFUL' ... GOODBYE, NOW...

E TO EXICO

C 1 6 68 BUD NEILL

'I WAS SOON RIGGED OUT AS A MEXICAN SHERIFF WI' A SADDLE AN' BRIDLE ON ELFIE ... AWFY SMART...'

I'LL AWA' OOT AN' HUNT THAE WICKED HILL BANDITS NOO!

'BUT WHILE I WAS UP IN THE HILLS HUNTIN' THE BANDITS, THE BANDITS WAS DOON IN THE VILLAGE ROBBIN' THE BANK ... RIGHT PESTS SO THEY WERE ...'

BANCO

C1 6 9 BUD NEILL

'AN' WHEN I WAS DOON IN THE VILLAGE PROTECTIN' THE BANK THE BANDITS WAS UP IN THE HILLS SHOUTIN' RUDE REMARKS AT ME ...'

NYAA-AA!

AWAY AN' WORK!

AW, THE FUNNY SHERIFF!

COME AND CATCH US, ONE-EYE!

AWFY ANNOYIN'

BANCO

'THEN WAN DAY MY CHANCE CAME ... I WAS IN MA OFFICE ...'

SENOR! THE BANK IS BEING ROBBED AGAIN ... COME QUICKLY!

$500 REWARD

'LIKE LIGHTNIN' I WAS OOT THE DOOR AN' UP AT THE BANK ...'

SIX VICIOUS BANDITS INSIDE SENOR ...THE WHOLE GANG—THROUGH THE DOOR AND FIRST RIGHT ... YOU CAN'T MISS 'EM ...

BANCO

THANKS, MAC!

'MY GUNS BLEEZIN', I WAS THROUGH THE DOOR IN A JIFFY...'

BANG!

BANG!

'I GOT FIVE O' THEM, BUT THE SIXTH WENT OOT THROUGH THE WINDAE'

QUICKLY, SENOR – THE LEADER, CORTEZ PANTZONANALE, IS ESCAPADO ... WHICH IS PRETTY DUFF MEXICANO

NED

TRY OUR PESOS

KEEP THE HEDRO-PEDRO!

RID INK

C1 7 0 BUD NEILL

'AFF I WENT IN PURSUIT ...'

STOP!

OUCH!

BASH!

TUMBLEWEED TUMBLING

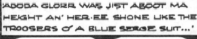

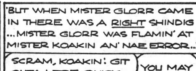

WHEN I LOOKED OWER THE HILL SEEN A TERRIBLE SIGHT...

WATTS KOAKIN AN' HIS RUSTLERS CHANGIN' THE LAZY Z BRAND TAE THE DIAMOND N ON MISTER GLORR'S NICE COOS!

COW POKE

THAT'S 50 HEAD WE DONE TONIGHT, BOSS!

FINE! WE'LL GIT' ALONG WITH THE LITTLE DOGIES TO THE DIAMOND N NOW ACROSS THE LONE PRAIREE-EE – WITH A YIPPEEE-AYE-A...

MOO MOO

SIZZLE

C1 7 9 BUD NEILL

'I HURRIED BACK TAE THE LAZY Z RANCH-HOOSE AN' WOKE UP MISTER GLORR...'

WATTS KOAKIN IS STEALIN' YIR NICE COOS, MR. GLORR! I'LL WAKE THE BOYS... PECH... WELL HIV TAE HURRY!

THE VARMINT! LET'S GO!

'WE GALLOPED OFF IN PURSUIT O' WATTS KOAKIN'S RUSTLERS AN' THE STOLEN COOS...'

RECKON THEY'LL BE IN COFFIN CANYON BY NOW! YOU BOYS GO ON THROUGH... DOSSER AND I WILL GO ROUND BY BLUE PINE PASS AND HEAD 'EM OFF!

OKAY BOSS!

'MISTER GLORR AN' ME GOT TAE THE TOP O' BLUE PINE PASS...'

THERE THEY ARE DOSSER: CAUGHT IN THE ACT!

WILL I BLATTER THEM THE NOO, MISTER GLORR?

NO... WAIT!

'WE SEEN THE REST O' THE LAZY Z BOYS COMIN' WHOOPIN' DOON COFFIN CANYON...'

KOAKIN'S GOT TO COME THIS WAY, DOSSER! HOLD YOUR FIRE!

AYE. OKAY!

C1 8 0 BUD NEILL

'IN A CLOUD O' DUST THE RUSTLERS THUNDERED PAST WI' THE HERD'

STOP, WATTS KOAKIN! YOU CAN'T ESCAPE! STOP OR I... GASP. GRUNT. GURGLE...

KOAKIN HAS SHOT MR GLORR!

'AS MR GLORR FELL TAE THE GRUN' WI' A BULLET THROUGH HIS BRAIN I WENT AFF IN PURSUIT O' WATTS KOAKIN, THE VICIOUS KILLER...'

I'LL GET YE FOR THAT, KOAKIN. IF I'VE TAE CHASE YE TAE CHINA! GET ON THERE ELFIE!

PERTICK?

GI BRIDE

'GALLOPIN' IN PURSUIT O' WATTS KOAKIN I LOOKED BACK AND SEEN THE LAZY Z BOYS COMIN' EFTER US BAD FIRE FOR LEATHER ...'

BASH ON, HEN – ATTA GIRL!

'SOON I WAS RIDIN' ALONGSIDE WATTS KOAKIN – HE COULDNAE SEE ME FOR THE STOOR ...'

NOO'S MA CHANCE!

C1 81BUD NEILL

'DINGIN' ALONG ABOOT SIXTY-MILE-AN-OOR I LEAPT FAE ELFIE'S BACK AN' KNOCKED KOAKIN AFF HIS HORSE – I WAS FLAMIN MAD AT WHIT HE'D DID TAE THE BOSS, D'YE SEE?'

THIS IS THE FEENISH O' YOU, YE MURDERIN' VILLAIN!

'BY THE TIME THE LAZY Z BOYS GOT UP I HAD WATTS KOAKIN A PRISONER ...'

WE GOT THE REST O' THEM PESKY RUSTLERS!

AN' THE STEERS!

NICE WORK. LOBEY!

LOBEY'S THE WEE BOY!

COME ON KOAKIN- YO'RE FOR THE LONG JUMP!

'BY THE TIME WE GOT BACK TO MR GLORR HE HAD RECOVERED ...'

JUST A SCRATCH, BOYS - A BULLET THROUGH MY BRAIN ... LET'S GIT ON HOME NOW ...

A HARDY YIN THAT!

'EFTER HAUNIN' OWER WATTS KOAKIN AN' HIS GANG TAE THE SHERIFF WE WENT BACK TAE THE RANCH ...'

HERE WE ARE THEN! JES' HANG UP YORE EMPTY SADDLES IN THE OL' CORRAL, BOYS - WITH A YIPPEE-AYE-A ...

'I HURRIT UP TAE THE COOK-HOOSE TAE SEE ADODA AN — WELL!'

OH, EXCUSE ME!

MY HUSBAND, MISTER LOBEY! HE'S ONE OF THE RANGERS - TEXAS RANGERS - AND HAS JES' GOT BACK FROM HIS HOLIDAYS ...

C1 82BUD NEILL

AND THIS IS MY FAMILY ... JESSIE, ANNIE, BESSIE, TOM, JAMES, TED, JACKIE, FRED, SUSIE, MAGGIE, JOE, MINNIE AN' THE TWINS, AMOS AND ANDY ...

CRACK!

'AFORE I COULD WARN THE LEADER, THE INJUNS SWOOPED DOON ON US WHOOPIN' LIKE BILLY-O ...'

WHOOP!

WHOOP!

WHOOP!

JUMPIN' THRO' A WHOOP

I MUST GET UP AN' WARN RANK BAJIN TAE GET THE WAGONS IN A CIRCLE-QUICK, ELFIE!

'EFTER SPEAKIN' TAE THE CRUEL LEADER O' THE PIONEERS I RODE BACK TAE THE END O' THE WAGONS'

WHIT'S THE NAME O' YIR LEADER, MAC?

BAJIN- RANK BAJIN- WE LOST OUR OWN CHIEF TWO DAYS AGO - SIOUX ARROW - THEN ALONG COMES THIS HOMBRE, BAJIN, AN' OFFERS TO TAKE US TO ARIZONA ...

LONG DOG

HE'S A NASTY-LOOKIN' PIECE O' WORK ...

HE SHORE IS, BUT THERE'S NOBODY ELSE KNOWS THE WAY TO ARIZONA ...

OH, I SEE!

'I RODE ALONG WI' THE COVERED WAGONS ALL NIGHT AN' AT SUN-UP A TERRIBLE THING HAPPENED ...'

GHOST RIDER IN THE SKY

o . o . O ...

INJUNS!

SIOUX INJUNS, BAJIN! GET YIR WAGONS TURNT ABOOT- LOOK SLIPPY NOO - HERE! GIE US THE RIBBONS-YE'RE LIKE A COO WI' A GUN!

'I GOT THE WAGONS INTAE A CIRCLE AN' WE PREPARED TAE FIGHT TAE THE LAST MAN ...'

GET THE WOMEN AN' WEANS IN THE CENTRE THERE! YOUSE BLOKES GET UNDER THE WAGONS AN' BLATTER THE INJUNS! COME ON, NOO- HURRY ALONG PLEASE!

'SOON THERE WERE THOOSANS O' INJUNS BITIN' THE DUST - AN' AWFY NOISE ...'

CRUNCH

CRUNCH

CRUNCH

CRUNCH

PRETTY GRITTY, HATCHET FACE

BUT DEFINITELY MOST UNPALATABLE, MUTTON HEAD

C 1 86 BUD NEILL

'LOOKIN' OOT THE CORNER O' MA GUID EE, I SEEN RANK BAJIN PREPARIN' TAE LEAVE THE PERTY ...'

WHY, THE BIG COOARD! RUNNIN' AWA' FAE THOOSANS O' FIERCE RIDSKINS! HI, YE BIG JESSIE— COME BACK!

DEID

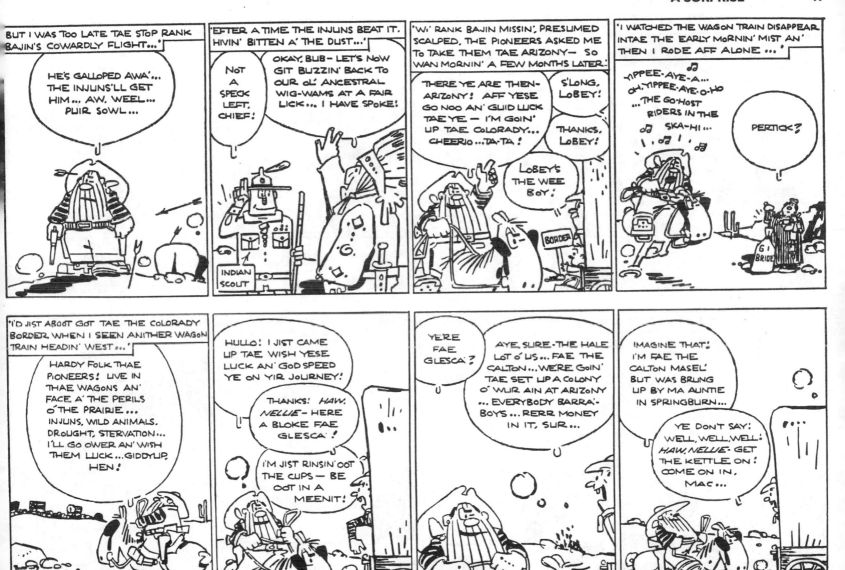

'BUT I HUDNAE TIME TAE STOP FOR MA TEA...'

NAW THANKS, MAC — I'M GOIN' UP TAE COLORADY AN' I'M IN A HURRY— SO I'LL JIST WISH YIR LEADER GUID LUCK THEN BEAT IT...

SUIT YIRSEL'— CHEERIO, THEN, AN' A' THE BEST...

'I GOT UP TAE THE LEADER'S WAGON...'

I JIST CAME TAE...

?

!

WE MEET AGAIN!

A FINE KIND O' A BLOKE YOU ARE — RUNNIN' AWA' FAE A FEW THOOSAN' INJUNS...

SELF-PRESERVATION IS A NATURAL LAW. MY FRIEND, AND I AM NOT PARTICULARLY ENAMOURED OF THE NOBLE RED MAN NOR OF HIS SCALPING PROPENSITIES...

WELL, I WAS GOIN' TAE COLORADY FOR SOME BEETLES— HEAR THE BRITISH MINISTRY O' AGRICULTURE'S LOOKIN' FOR'S MANY AS THEY CAN GET— BUT I'M NO' GOIN' NOO WI' YOU LEADIN' THE PERTY, BAJIN...

'THE PIONEERS FAE CALTON HAD PICKED UP RANK BAJIN WHO'D PROMISED TO TAKE THEM TAE ARIZONY...'

NAW!

WELL, I NEVER!

COWARDY CUSTARD!

THEN HE RAN AWA' FAE THE SIOUX...

WELL, YOU JIST COME ON WI' US LOBEY AN' KEEP YIR EE ON HIM...

'WE SOON CROSSED THE BORDER INTAE ARIZONY...'

AW, THE PUIR SOWL!

GIE 'ER A LIFT...

A WEAN, TAE!

ARIZONA TATE LINE   NOT STATE

PERTICK?

GI BRIDE

'WE GIE'D THE LADY FAE PERTICK A HURL— AN' THAT NIGHT WE CAME TAE A RIVER...'

SMASHIN' WEE SPOT, THIS...

AYE, WHIT ABOOT SETTIN' UP WUR COLONY OWER THERE AT THE CREEK...

COME ON WE'LL GET STERTED...

'ALL NIGHT LONG THE WOODS RANG WI' THE BLOWS O' AXES, AN' IN THE MORNIN'...'

THERE WE ARE NOO, THEN— CALTON CREEK!

A' WE NEED IS A JILE AN' A SALOON...

'IN A COUPLE O' WEEKS WE WERE A' SETTLED DOON IN CALTON CREEK ...'

THE PLACE IS FEENISHED NOO... POST OFFICE, SHOE-MAKER, GROCER, BUTCHER, STABLES, GAMBLER, GUN-SMITH, PLUMBER, SALOON, AN' A JILE ... A' WE NEED NOO IS A SHERIFF!

THERE'S NAEBODY TAE BATE LOBEY!

LOBEY'LL BE THE SHERIFF!

WE WANT LOBEY!

LOBEY'S THE WEE BOY!

'...AN' SO IT WAS I BECAME THE SHERIFF O' CALTON CREEK ...'

POLIS SPORTS

WANTED FOR MURDER

'... WI' RANK BAJIN AS RESIDENT VILLAIN ...'

HEE HEE HEE

'... AN' THE HITCH-HIKER ALWAYS SOMEWHERE ABOOT TRYIN' TAE THUMB A RIDE HAME ...'

PERTICK?

NED

B.I. BRIDE

WELL, THERE YE ARE NOO! HIV ANITHER JUJUBE AN' RUN AWA' AN' DON'T GIE ONY MAIR CHEEK TAE YIR ELDERS, LIKE GUID WEE BOYS ...

WE WON'T, MISTER DOSSER ...

THANKS, MISTER DOSSER ...

SHERIFF

WAN JUJUBE LEFT AN' I HUD A HALE QUARTER WHEN I STERTED TELLIN' THEM MA STORY! WEANS CAN FAIRLY WIRE INTAE THE SWEETIES, TUT-TUT-TUT, AYE, RIGHT ENOUGH ...

SHERIFF

RERR BOOK THIS ... A' ABOOT COWBOYS AN' INJUNS ... SUCK, SUCK, SUCK ...

TRUE WESTERN

SHERIFF

ZZZZ

THE END

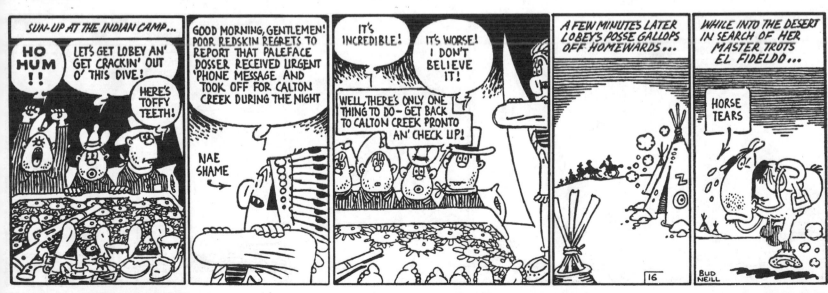

AT THE INDIAN CAMP...

BY THIS TIME DOSSER'S BONES WILL HAVE BEEN PICKED CLEAN BY VULTURES!!! NOTHING NOW STANDS IN MY WAY!! I'LL SEE TOFFY TEETH AND GET HIS ASSISTANCE WITH MY NEXT DASTARDLY DESIGN!

GOOD MORNING! I HAVE ANOTHER NEFARIOUS PLAN WITH WHICH YOU CAN HELP ME, T.T.!

SHOOT, KID!

IT IS NONE OTHER THAN A PROJECT TO HAVE YOUR BRAVES GO ON THE WARPATH AND CAPTURE CALTON CREEK — THEN I SHALL APPOINT MYSELF SHERIFF AND BE AS VILLAINOUS AS I LIKE!

YOU CAN BE MAYOR!

21

GEE! THAT'S GREAT! I'LL TELL THE BRAVES TO GET THEIR TOMAHAWKS SHARPENED RIGHT AWAY!

BUD NEILL

A VULTURE'S SHADDY! I'LL NO' GIVE IN! I'LL HAE ANITHER WEE CRAWL AN' SEE IF I CAN FIN' WATTER — NAE AULD VULTURE'S GONNAE EAT ME ...

TEN MINUTES LATER ...

IT'S SURELY NO' TRUE! IT CANNA' BE RIGHT!

IT'S STILL THERE!

IT'S RIGHT ENOUGH!

A WATTER HOLE!

SAVED!

INSTALLED FOR YOUR CONVENIENCE by DESERT WATER HOLES, Inc.

SOAP

22

BUD NEILL

CONFIDENT IN HIS DISGUISE, TOFFY TEETH'S PAWNEE SCOUT HAS ENTERED CALTON CREEK...

YA LOOK MIGHTY SUSPICIOUS, STRANGER — WHAT'S YER NAME?

KOHLER!

KOHLER, EH? YA LOOK DARN LIKE A REDSKIN TO ME... BEHIND ALL THAT PHONEY PHACE PHUNGUS YOU'RE PURTY HIGHLY-COLOURED...

YEAH— HE'LL BE TECKNY KOHLER!

MIGHTY FINE!

ANYWAY, YOU OUGHT TO BE ASHAMED OF YOURSELF SNOOPING ABOUT LIKE THIS! YOU'VE NOTHING TO BE PROUD OF! YOU'RE SHAMEFUL ...IGNOMINIOUS ... UNRENOWNED ... NOT CELEBRATED...

INGLORIOUS TECKNY KOHLER!

MIGHTY FINE!

NOW, SCRAM! TAKE OFF! SKEDADDLE! GET OUT OF THE CREEK PRONTO OR I'LL FILL YA SO FULL O' LEAD YOU'LL LOOK LIKE A LACE CURTAIN! ON YOUR WAY, MAC! GIT!

BURNING HATE

FIZZ

BUD NEILL

AT THE DESERT WATER HOLE, LOBEY IS SLAKING HIS THIRST...

INSTALLED FOR YOUR CONVENIENCE by DESERT WATER HOLES, INC.

GURGLE ... GURGLE ... GURGLE

THAT WAS SMASHIN'! NOO I'LL HIV TAE FIGGER OOT HOW TAE GIT BACK TAE CALTON CREEK...

?

ELFIE!

LOBEY!

OH, DASH IT! I'M NOT SUPPOSED TO TALK...

THAT'S ALL RIGHT— I'LL LET YE AFF THIS TIME!

BUD NEILL

DAWN BREAKS OVER CALTON CREEK

MOAN! GROAN! GASP!

STRANGE SOUNDS, INDEED! I MUST INVESTIGATE ...

IT WAS THAT STRANGER I CHASED OUT OF THE CREEK THE OTHER NIGHT... MOAN... CAME BACK WHEN I WAS SLEEPIN' AN' BEAT ME UP... GROAN... HE WAS A PAWNEE SCOUT AFTER ALL... ...GASP...

THAR'S A-GOIN' TO BE TROUBLE WIT' THE INJUNS... MOAN... I KIN SMELL IT... GROAN... THAT PAWNEE WURN'T HANGIN' AROUND THE CREEK JIST LOOKIN' FOR CIGARETTES ...GASP... WISH LOBEY'D GIT BACK...

WAS THIS PAWNEE WHO ATTACKED YOU CLEAN SHAVEN?

NO...HIS FACE WAS COVERED WITH LONG HAIR...

OH- A SHETLAND PAWNEE?

MIGHTY FINE!

ON SATURDAY AT SUN-UP WE ATTACK CALTON CREEK ...

THAT'S AWFULLY EARLY, CHIEF!

TRUE... BUT THE STORY HAS GOT TO MAKE THE EARLY EDITIONS OF THE 'EVENING TIMES'

UNFORTUNATELY, WE HAVE NOT SUFFICIENT MUSTANGS TO GO AROUND. SOME OF YOU WILL HAVE TO TRAVEL BY STAGE-COACH. I WILL PAY FOR YOUR TICKETS, BUT YOUR SQUAWS WILL HAVE TO PAY FOR THEMSELVES ... ASK ME WHY.

WHY ???

BECAUSE NONE BUT THE BRAVES DESERVE THE FARE ...

QUITE A WAG, THE CHIEF!

BRAVO!

GET THE POLIS!

IN THE DESERT, LOBEY & EL FIDELDO ARE ENDEAVOURING TO GET BACK TO CALTON CREEK...

I'VE NAE IDEA WHAUR WE ARE, ELFIE — DOOT WE'RE LOST...

FOUR HOURS LATER...

THIS IS ALL RANK BAJIN'S FAULT! WAIT TILL I GET MA HAUN'S ON THAT BANDY-LEGGIT BABOON!

SIX HOURS LATER...

CHUG! CHUG! CHUG!

WHIT'S THAT?

DESERT RAT (DOON A HOLE)

HOPELESSLY LOST, LOBEY LISTENS TO THE MYSTERIOUS SOUND IN THE DISTANCE, UNAWARE THAT IN THE FOOTHILLS to THE NORTH of CALTON CREEK THE INDIANS ARE 'RISING...

GOSHDARN IT! TIME TO GET UP AGAIN, BOYS!

BRR-RR-R

29

BUD NEILL

IN THE GREY LIGHT OF DAWN, TOFFY TEETH'S FEROCIOUS BRAVES ARE LINED UP IN BATTLE FORMATION OUTSIDE CALTON CREEK — THE WHOLE SIX OF THEM...

(SHORTAGE of SPACE PROHIBITS THE INCLUSION of MORE)

HOW! HOW! HOW! HOW!
HOW! HOW! HOW!

WAR PAINT QUICK DRYING

HULLO, MRS THOMSON — THOUGHT YE'D HAE BEEN AWA' AT MURRAYFIELD THE DAY...

NO' ME, NAW — I'D RAITHER BE SCALPED BY TOFFY TEETH THAN SPEN' A DAY IN EDINBURY...

MA GUID TWELVE-AN'-A-TANNER BUNNET!

ZING

AN ARRY!

RUN FOR YIR LIVES! THE INDIANS HIV ROSE!

HELP!

MITHER!

BRAVO!

30

BUD NEILL

CHUG
CHUG
CHUG

A WEE BLACK SPECK ON THE HORIZON!

IT'S COMIN' NEARER AN' NEARER...

I CAN SEE WHIT IT IS NOO!

FIRST TIME I EVER FOUND WAN WHEN I WANTED IT...

IS THAT NO' GREAT!

TAXI!

31

BUD NEILL

THE HEROIC DEFENDERS OF CALTON CREEK ARE FIGHTING GRIMLY AGAINST TOFFY TEETH'S SAVAGE BRAVES...

THERE'S A BLOW TAE WUR MORALE IF EVER I SEEN WAN — THEY'VE SET FIRE TAE THE SALOON!

THEY GOT ME, PAL!

WE'RE RUNNING OUT OF AMMUNITION! WE MUST FALL BACK AND FIGHT DESPERATELY AGAINST OVERWHELMING ODDS!

YE'RE DARN TOOTIN', PARDNER!

THE HARDY PIONEER WOMENFOLK OF THE OLD WEST FIGHT STOICALLY BY THE SIDES OF THEIR HARDY PIONEER MENFOLK...

HAUD THAT YIN, YE BOW-LEGGIT WEE BAUCHLE!

AN' THERE'S WAN FOR YOU, HAWKEYE!

TEX

I SHOT AN ARROW IN THE AIR, IT FELL TAE EARTH I KNOW NOT WHERE...

AN' WHIT IS MAIR, SHE DISNAE CARE— FOR SHE'S MAIR ARROWS UP THE STAIR...

MIGHTY FINE!

32

BUD NEILL

LOBEY IS CLOSING IN ON RANK BAJIN...

THIS OLD TREE IS THE ONLY BRIDGE ACROSS YONDER YAWNING CHASM!

IDEA

STOP, BAJIN, IN THE NAME O' THE LOBEY!

DOSSER'S GAINING! I SHALL JUST HAVE TIME TO CARRY OUT MY NEFARIOUS PLAN ON THE OTHER SIDE OF THIS MAKESHIFT BRIDGE!

DANGER YAWNING CHASM TERRIBLE DEEP

WHAT LUCK! A SAW! I SHALL SAW THROUGH THE LOG BRIDGE AND DOSSER'S WEIGHT WILL CAUSE IT TO COLLAPSE, HURLING HIM ON TO THE JAGGED ROCKS THOUSANDS OF FEET BELOW!!!

THERE NOW! MY EVIL WORK IS DONE! HERE COMES DOSSER! I MUST BE OFF!

BUD NEIL

WILL LOBEY FALL INTO THE TERRIBLE YAWNING CHASM WHEN THE BRIDGE COLLAPSES? LOOK OUT FOR A FURTHER THRILLING INSTALMENT TOMORROW.

41

GALLOPING LIKE MAD IN PURSUIT OF RANK BAJIN, LOBEY APPROACHES THE LOG BRIDGE ACROSS THE YAWNING CHASM UNAWARE THAT IT HAS BEEN TAMPERED WITH BY RANK...

BUD NEIL

GETTING RIGHT EXCITING THIS— AIN'T IT?

42

IN CALTON CREEK...

NOO THAT THE INDIAN RISING HAS FIZZLED OOT, THE PRESIDENT'S WITHDREW THE ERMED FORCES — THEY ALL WENT AWA' THIS MORNIN'...

THANK GUIDNESS, TAE! THAE GEE-EYES!

AWFY FELLIES, SO THEY ARE, AYE! WAN O' THEM GIE'D ME A BIG PACKET O' BREAKFAST FOOD, BUT IT DISNAE SUIT ME...

AW, THE SHAME!

IT'S NICE ENOUGH TASTED, MIND YE...

AYE?

BUT IT GIE'S ME AWFY HICCUPS...

ANOTHER OF THESE AIR-RAISING CEREALS?

MIGHTY FINE!

43

LOBEY & EL FIDELDO APPROACH THE TREACHEROUS LOG BRIDGE OVER THE YAWNING CHASM...

? ?

CRACK!

RANK BAJIN'S DASTARDLY PLAN HAS SUCCEEDED! THE BRIDGE IS BROKE! ...INTO THE YAWNING CHASM FALLS LOBEY & EL FIDELDO! IT SURE LOOKS LIKE CURTAINS FOR THE INTREPID SHERIFF THIS TIME, DON'T IT?

44

THREE DAYS LATER, RANK BAJIN REVISITS THE SCENE OF HIS CRIME...

EUREKA! THAT IS THE END OF DOSSER! HE WILL HAVE BEEN SHATTERED INTO THOUSANDS OF PIECES ON THESE JAGGED ROCKS BELOW! THUS PERISH ALL WHO GET IN THE PATH OF RANK BAJIN, VILLAIN!

HAPPY THAT HE IS AT LAST RID OF LOBEY, BAJIN CANTERS OFF INTO THE NIGHT SINGING GAILY...

OH, I'D LIKE TO GET YA ON A SLOW BOAT TO CHINA ALL TO MYSELF AH-LONE... TUM-TEE-TUM TEE-TUM

WHILE STILL FALLING THROUGH SPACE ARE LOBEY AND EL FIDELDO... REMEMBER THIS IS A VERY DEEP CHASM

UPSIDE DOON, INT IT?

I'VE BEEN FALLIN' THROUGH SPACE FOR THREE DAYS NOO WI' NO' A BITE TAE EAT! I'M STERVIN'!

BAJIN, TOO, IS BEGINNING TO FEEL THE PANGS OF HUNGER...

NOBODY LIVES ON THESE MOUNTAINS! I SHALL DESCEND TO THE VALLEY AND THERE STICK UP SOME POOR FARMER AND STEAL HIS MEAGRE RATIONS!

45

DOWN IN THE VALLEY A SMALL FARMER IS TRYING TO WREST A LIVING FROM THE STONEY SOIL...

DANGBUST IT, MAW, BUT THIS SHORE IS STONEY SOIL TO TRY TO WREST A LIVIN' FROM!

IF I DIDN'T COME FROM HARDY PIONEER STOCK I'D QUIT WRESTLIN' AN' JIST REST — VERY GOOD JOKE, HO-HO-HO-HO!

LAWSH A'MIGHTY, PETE — THERE'S MORE DANGBOOZLED STONES IN THIS 'ERE SOIL THAN THERE IS IN A BAG OF GLASGOW COAL!

WELL, BINGDAST IT, MAW — I AIN'T A-DOIN' NO MORE WRESTLIN' THIS MAWNIN' SO LEAVE US NOW ADJOURN TO OUR DELAPIDATED SHACK AN' GIT AN EARFUL OF 'HOUSEWIVES' CHOICE'!

BOOMDOOZLE IT, PETE, — NOW YOU'RE REALLY COOKIN' WIT' GAS!

LATER...

THET DOOMBAZZLED 'CUCKOO WALTZ' IS SHORE GITTIN' IN THIS SMALL FARMER'S HAIR, MAW!

MINE, TOO, PETE — BUT I THINK WE GOT COMPANY!

REACH FOR THE CEILING!

46

EL FIDELDO HAS SNEAKED UP BEHIND RANK BAJIN WHO IS THREATENING LOBEY WITH A GUN...

EL FIDELDO IS LIMBERING UP — THE TENSION IS TERRIFIC!

EL FIDELDO LETS GO WITH HIS RIGHT— BANG ON THE SEAT OF BAJIN'S WELL-PRESSED PANTS!

BASH!

THANKS, ELFIE, BUT YE SHOULDNAE HIV KICKED HIM SO HARD! HE'S WENT OOT O' SIGHT AN' NOO WE'LL HIV TAE GO AN' LOOK FOR THE PEST AGAIN!

BLUSH BLUSH

51

LOBEY IS LOOKING FOR RANK BAJIN WHO HAS BEEN KICKED OUT OF SIGHT BY EL FIDELDO...

NAE SIGN O' HIM, ELFIE, AN' WE'VE BEEN RIDIN' FOR TWO DAYS NOO — WE'LL ASK THIS WEE GEEZER IF HE'S SEEN BAJIN!

HULLO, WEE GEEZER! HIV YE SEEN ONYTHIN' STRANGE FLEEIN' THROUGH THE AIR THIS PAST DAY OR TWO?

YUS! I SEEN A PECULIAR BLACK OBJECT ZIPPING ALONG ABOUT 2,000 FEET IN THAT DIRECTION THIS MAWNIN'! LIKE A BAT OUT O' THE BAD FIRE HE WAS GOIN' TOO, STRANGER!

THANKS, WEE GEEZER!

YE MUST HAE GIE'D HIM AN AWFY WALLOP, ELFIE — BUT WE'RE NO' THAT FAUR AFF CALTON CREEK NOO, SO WE'LL JIST GET AWA' HAME AN' TELL THEM WHIT'S HAPPENED!

52

LOBEY IS HOMEWARD BOUND...

THAT WIS AWFY BAD LUCK LOSSIN' RANK BAJIN EFTER A' WUR TROUBLE, BUT IT CANNAE BE HELPED NOO!

PERTICK?

NAW!

AW, THE SHAME!

WELL, HIV YE ONYTHIN' GUID FOR THE 'GRAND NATIONAL' THE MORRA'?

!

53

LOBEY ARRIVES BACK AT CALTON CREEK ...

HERE'S LOBEY! NEVER LET ON ABOOT YON!

NAW, NEVER LET DAB!

HELLO, LOBEY! NICE DAY!

NO' SAE NICE! I'VE WENT AN' LOST BAJIN AGAIN! ELFIE KICKED HIM OOT O' SIGHT! AH, WEEL—I'LL JIST AWA' INTAE MA OFFICE AN' HAE A WEE READ AT 'TAMMY TROOT' IN THE 'BULLETIN' —CHEERIO!

L. DOSSER SHERIFF

RANK BAJIN!

SHERIFF

54

AYE- HE LANDED IN THE HIGH STREET THIS MORNIN' AN' THE BOYS TIED HIM UP UNTIL YE GOT BACK!

HE LOOKS AS THOUGH HE'D FELL OWER BECHER'S BROOK!

GUID AULD ELFIE!

Bild NEILL

KICKED BACK TO CALTON CREEK BY EL FIDELDO, RANK BAJIN IS NOW LANGUISHING IN JAIL. AND HIS LANGUISH IS HORRIBLE...

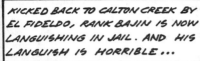

WEE PUFFS OF BLUE SMOKE

CURSES! HAD IT NOT BEEN FOR THAT TWO-LEGGED EQUINE OAF I WOULD NOW BE CREATING ALARM AND DESPONDENCY THROUGHOUT THE 48 STATES! AND IT'S ALL THAT SMART ALEC DOSSER'S FAULT TOO — THE MEDDLING, MUTTON-HEADED, WALL-EYED ▄▄ ▄▄▄ ▄▄

MAIR BAD WORDS, TUT, TUT, TUT...

DOSSER? I WONDER WHAT HE PLANS TO DO WITH ME NOW... PROBABLY TRY ME AND GIVE ME TWENTY YEARS IN THE JUG! ALCATRAZ OR SING-SING! OH, TUSH 'N FIDDLE — WHAT A THOUGHT! THAT DOSSER...

55

HOW I'D LIKE TO GET HIM ALONE FOR FIVE MINUTES — ALL TO MYSELF!

ON A SLOW BOAT TO CHINA?

MIGHTY FINE!

WRAPPED IN THOUGHT, LOBEY IS PONDERING WHAT TO DO WITH RANK BAJIN...

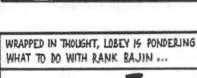

BEST QUALITY THOUGHT WRAPPINGS

PONDER

PONDER

PONDER

OUTSIDE LOBEY'S OFFICE...

WE'RE JIST WAITIN' TAE SEE WHIT LOBEY IS GONNAE DAE WI' RANK BAJIN...

NUTHIN'S BAD ENOUGH FOR YON YIN...

WHEESHT! KINDLY DISCERN THE SOUND OF FOOTSTEPS APPROACHING THE DOOR... IT'LL BE LOBEY WITH FATEFUL TIDINGS, NAE DOOT!

Bild NEILL

FRIENDS, I HAVE NOW DECIDED THAT RANK BAJIN SHALL BE TRIED AT THE CALTON CREEK COORT WHICH WILL .... GURGLE GURGLE GURGLE

THE REST OF LOBEY'S ANNOUNCEMENT HAS BEEN DROWNED IN APPLAUSE

56

AULD RANK'S FOR IT THIS TIME — HE'S TAE GO TAE THE COORT...

YUS

IF I WIS LOBEY I'D JIST SEN' HIM AWA' FAE THE CREEK AN' TELL HIM NEVER TAE COME BACK...

YUS YUS

BUT WHA' ELSE WID HIV HIM ? HE'S THAT DIRTY-LOOKIN' WI' THAT BLACK HOOD O' HIS...

YUS YUS YUS

WE'D HIV TAE SEN' HIM TAE LIVE WI' FOLKS AS DIRTY-LOOKIN' AS HIMSEL' — THEN THEY WIDNAE NOTICE HIM

MAKING THE BANISHMENT FIT THE GRIME ?

MIGHTY FINE!

57

AT LOBEY'S OFFICE...

WELL, THAT'S THE DETAILS A' TOOK CARE O' — BAJIN'S TRIAL WILL STERT THE MORRA ! I'LL JIST AWA' OWER TAE THE JILE NOO AN' SEE EVERYTHIN'S ALL RIGHT...

LATER: AT THE JILE...

EVERYTHIN' OKAY, JACK ?

YUP: NEVER TAKE MY EYES OFF DIS CHUMP — HE'S SLIPPERY AS A NEILL, I MEAN AN EEL ...

DIS MAWNIN' FOUR LITTLE BLACK GEEZERS COME ALONG WIT' A BIG LOAF FOR POPPA HERE, BUT I CHASED THEM FOR THEIR LIVES — ONCE BIT, TWICE SHY !

THAT'S RIGHT, JACK!

I GOT HIM MANACLED ON TO THE WALL, LOBEY, SO DO NOT FEAR — BAJIN WILL BE AT THE COURT TOMORROW OR MY NAME AIN'T JACK !

OKAV, JACK!

58

THE TRIAL of RANK BAJIN...

ORDER!

... RANK BAJIN, DESCRIBED IN THE INDICTMENT AS 'VILLAIN', YOU ARE ARRAIGNED BEFORE THIS 'ERE COORT TO ANSWER FOR YOUR HEINOUS CRIMES AGAINST SOCIETY. THESE CRIMES ARE LISTED AS FOLLOWS, TO WIT, VIZ., AN' THAT IS TO SAY...

HEINOUS?

YEAH — THEY MAKE THE BAKED BEINOUS...

TWO HOURS LATER...

... AN' THAT, FIVE-HUNDRED-AN'-SIXTY-SEVENTHLY, YOU DID ON THE AFTERNOON OF JANUARY 24 HOLD UP AND ASSAULT HIS MAJESTY'S MAIL RIDER, ONE TUFFY O'TOOLE, AND STEAL THE MAIL WHICH CONTAINED GOLD DUST TO SAY NOTHING OF WUR POOLS COUPONS...

... THE COORT WILL BE GRATIFIED TAE LEARN THAT, BEING A DUNTOCHER O'TOOLE, TUFFY HAS NOW MADE A GOOD RECOVERY FROM HIS HARROWING EXPERIENCE...

LOUD APPLAUSE FROM ALL QUARTERS

59

YE'RE A PEST, BAJIN... THERE ISNAE WAN WORD CAN BE SAID IN YIR FAVOUR... YE'VE NAE SCRUPLES... YE'RE COMPLETELY DISHONEST... YE'RE A THIEF AN' A ROGUE...

YE'VE SET OOT ON A LIFE O' CRIME AN' IT'LL NO' BE TOLERATED BY THE CITIZENS O' THIS TOON! I'M GOIN' TAE MAKE AN EXAMPLE O' YE...

... AS A DETERRENT TAE OTHERS AN' AS PROOF THAT CRIME DISNAE PAY I CANNAE DAE ELSE THAN IMPOSE A PENALTY WHICH WILL MAKE YE BRIGHTEN UP YIR IDEAS A BIT AN' LEAD A MAIR LAW-ABIDIN' LIFE IN THE FUTURE... COUGH, COUGH...

TEN BOB-AN' FOURTEEN DAYS TAE PAY!

CULLAPSE OF POLIS

LOBEY WASN'T A GLASGOW MAGISTRATE FOR TWO YEARS FOR NOTHIN'...

YOU SAID IT, KID!

THE END

60

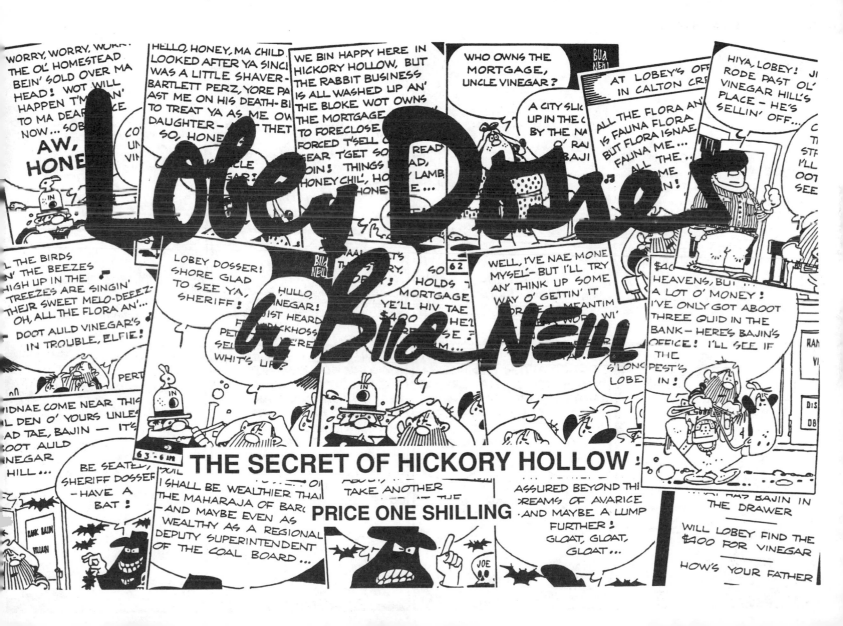

THE SECRET OF HICKORY HOLLOW

PRICE ONE SHILLING

Today starts a new adventure featuring Legal-Eagle Dosser & his equine biped, El Fideldo...

It is a simple tale of love & heroism set amid the scenic splendour of the old west.   Our story opens at a small farm near Calton Creek which is under the hammer...Lights, cameras, auction...

WHAT AM I BID FOR THESE TWO RABBITS?

TWO BUCKS

IS THAT A BID OR A QUESTION?

HICKORY HOLLOW — V. HILL — RABBIT FARMER

TWO BUCKS? WHY, I GOT A DOLLAR SEVENTY-FIVE FOR THE LADY RABBIT — SHE WEIGHED TWENNY-NINE POUNDS!

THAT'S A LOTTA DOE, MISTER!

NOW HERE'S SOMETHIN'! A NICE PARCEL OF FOUR BUNNIES AND A GRASS-CUTTING MACHINE TO ANYONE WHO CAN TELL WHAT WELL-KNOWN PIANO DUO THE PARCEL REPRESENTS...

RABBITZ AN' LANMOWER?

SAM PAN: THE NEW COMIC

VELLY GLOOT, SLAM!

61 - 4 APR

WORRY, WORRY, WORRY! THE OL' HOMESTEAD BEIN' SOLD OVER MA HEAD! WOT WILL HAPPEN T'ME AN' TO MA DEAR NIECE NOW... SOB...

AW, HONEY!

COMIN', UNCLE VINEGAR!

HICKORY HO — V. HILL- RABBIT FARM

HELLO, HONEY, MA CHILD! I'VE LOOKED AFTER YA SINCE YA WAS A LITTLE SHAVER — OL' BARTLETT PERZ, YORE PAPPY, AST ME ON HIS DEATH-BED TO TREAT YA AS ME OWN DAUGHTER — AIN'T THET SO, HONEY?

YUS, UNCLE VINEGAR!

WE BIN HAPPY HERE IN HICKORY HOLLOW, BUT THE RABBIT BUSINESS IS ALL WASHED UP AN' THE BLOKE WOT OWNS THE MORTGAGE IS GOIN' TO FORECLOSE — SO I BIN FORCED T'SELL OFF ME GEAR T'GET SOME READY COIN! THINGS IS BAD, HONEY CHIL', HONEY LAMB, HONEY PIE...

SNIFF!

WHO OWNS THE MORTGAGE, UNCLE VINEGAR?

A CITY SLICKER UP IN THE CREEK BY THE NAME O' RANK BAJIN!

62 - 5 APR

...THAT IS THE POSITION, THEN! I AM WITHIN THE LAW IN FORECLOSING THE MORTGAGE ON HILL'S PLACE IF HE FAILS TO PAY ME $400 — THERE IS NOTHING YOU CAN DO ABOUT IT, SHERIFF!

YE'RE RIGHT, BAJIN — BUT YE'RE STILL A WICKED SCAMP PITTIN' AULD HILL AN' HONEY PERZ OOT O' HICKORY HOLLOW — TO SAY NOTHIN' O' ALL THAE PUIR WEE RABBITS! YEVE NAE HERT!

GOOD-DAY... AND MIND YOUR HEAD ON THE MUMMY ON YOUR WAY OUT!

LATER..

IMAGINE ME BEIN BASTED BY BEJIN — I MEAN BESTED BY BAJIN! I'LL HIV TAE GET THE MONEY FOR AULD VINEGAR SOMEHOW ... THINK, THINK WORRY...

HEE-HEE-HEE! IT DID MY STONEY OLD HEART GOOD TO SEE DOSSER'S FACE JUST NOW! HE'S FRANKLY WORRIED, COMMA, HE'S FRANKLY WORRIED...

YOU'RE RIGHT, RANK — HE'S FRANKIE WORRIED, COMO!

VELLY GLOOT, SLAM!

65 - 8 APR

WITH HICKORY HOLLOW I CAN MAKE MY FORTUNE! LITTLE DOES HILL KNOW OF WHAT RICHES LIE UNDER THE SOIL! ONCE IN POSSESSION I SHALL BE WEALTHIER THAN THE MAHARAJA OF BARODA — AND MAYBE EVEN AS WEALTHY AS A REGIONAL DEPUTY SUPERINTENDENT OF THE COAL BOARD...

I HAVE PUT IT SAFELY AWAY IN THIS DRAWER — MY PASSPORT TO OPULENCE! I'LL MAKE SURE THERE ARE NO SNOOPERS ABOUT, THEN I SHALL TAKE ANOTHER GANDER AT THE OBJECT...

JOE

BEAUTIFUL! SUPERB! MY FORTUNE IS ASSURED BEYOND THE DREAMS OF AVARICE — AND MAYBE A LUMP FURTHER! GLOAT, GLOAT, GLOAT...

JOE

WHAT IS THE SECRET OF HICKORY HOLLOW
———
WHAT HAS BAJIN IN THE DRAWER
———
WILL LOBEY FIND THE $400 FOR VINEGAR
———
HOW'S YOUR FATHER
———

AT HICKORY HOLLOW

THINGS IS LOOKIN' PRETTY BLACK, VINEGAR — WE'VE TAE FIN' ANITHER $200 BY NOON THE MORRA'! AWFY CAUL' GOT ALL O' A SUDDEN, HASN'T IT?

SURE HAS, LOBEY — HARD FROST

BRRRR — IT'S NIPPY! HOO MANY RABBITS HIV YE LEFT, VINEGAR?

4,538!

AT RANK BAJIN'S OFFICE

TOMORROW IS DER TAG! TOMORROW HICKORY HOLLOW WILL BE MINE! I SHALL NOW GET IN TOUCH WITH MY CROOKED LAWYER, KING, AND ASK HIM TO BE HERE AT NOON! GOSH, BUT IT'S COLD...

MY CROOKED LAWYER, KING, IS A MASTER OF OBSTRUCTION BY QUIBBLE AND OF DECEIT BY VERBAL SUBTERFUGE — HE IS A PERSON EXPERT IN PUTTING FORWARD PLAUSIBLE BUT ESSENTIALLY FALLACIOUS ARGUMENTS...

CHICANE A LA KING?

VELLY GLOOT, SLAM!

71 15-4

IT IS FIVE MINUTES TO NOON, CROOKED LAWYER KING ... THE SANDS ARE RUNNING OUT FOR MISTER VINEGAR HILL, I'M AFRAID! HO-HO-HO!

THREE MINUTES TO NOON! HERE COMES SOMEBODY NOW — JUST WAIT TILL YOU SEE HILL'S FACE STREAMING WITH TEARS AS HE PLEADS FOR MERCY! HEE-HEE-HEE!

THERE'S YIR $400, BAJIN! HICKORY HOLLOW IS AULD VINEGAR'S NOO, SO SEE US THE TITLE DEEDS AN' LOOK SLIPPY...

$400 CASH! IT'S IMPOSSIBLE! HOW DID YOU GET THE MONEY?

LAST NIGHT WAS AWEY FROSTY — WE LET VINEGAR'S RABBITS OOT O' THE HUTCHES AN' MADE 'EM SIT ABOOT OOTSIDE ALL NIGHT — THIS MORNIN' WE SELLT THE HALE JING-BANG TAE A GLESCA FISHMONGER FOR THE BALANCE O' WHIT WE NEEDED TAE PAY YE...

FROZEN RABBITS! CURSES — FOILED AGAIN!

72 16-4

OH, TUSH! MY NEFARIOUS PLAN TO GET HICKORY HOLLOW IN MY CLUTCHES HAS BEEN BROUGHT TO NOUGHT BY DOSSER AND HIS FROZEN RABBITS—BUT WAIT! I HAVE YET ANOTHER NEFARIOUS PLAN—AND THIS TIME I WON'T FAIL!

THIS NEW NEFARIOUS PLAN OF MINE IS REALLY A PIPPIN! I CAN'T MISS! MY TWISTED BRAIN IS WORKING OVERTIME AND VERY SOON NOW I SHALL BE IN POSSESSION OF HICKORY HOLLOW AND OF THE PLUTONIUM!

I'M NO GREAT SHAKES AS A LOOKER, BUT MY HYPNOTIC EYES ARE VERY HIGH-POWERED INDEED!

I'LL PUT ON MY LIGHT-WEIGHT SUMMER HOOD WITH THE DRAPE SHAPE AND THE HAND-STITCHED EYE-HOLES, BRUSH MY TEETH, PRESS MY PANTS, AND GIVE MYSELF A GOOD GOING-OVER WITH A CLOTHES BRUSH—THEN I SHALL BE ABSOLUTELY IRRESISTIBLE!

73 18-4

AT HICKORY HOLLOW...
AIN'T THAT GREAT, UNCLE VINEGAR—HICKORY HOLLOW OUR VERY OWN AT LAST, THANKS TO DEAR MISTER DOSSER! AIN'T THAT JES' DANDY! I SHALL NOW BE ABLE TO GAMBOL AMID THE FLOWERS IN THE MEADOW TO MY LITTLE HEART'S CONTENT—OH, JOY! GOODY, GOODY, GOODY!

THET'S RIGHT, HONEY!

EXCUSE ME, UNCLE, WHILE I NOW GO AND GAMBOL WITH MY PLAYMATES IN THE BARN...

OKAY, HONEY!

YESTERDAY SHE TOOK FIFTY CENTS OFF 'EM AT PONTOON

ON HER WAY DOWN TO THE BARN, HONEY ESPIES A LONE HORSEMAN APPROACHING—SHE KNOWS HE'S A LONE HORSEMAN BECAUSE THERE IS NOBODY WITH HIM AND HE IS ON A HORSE. HONEY IS NO DOPE...

GOOD MORNING, FAIR HONEY! YOU GET MORE BEAUTIFUL EVERY DAY, WHAT ARE YOU DOING THIS EVENING, AND IF YOUR DEAR UNCLE SHOULD SNUFF IT WOULD YOU BE LEFT THE FARM IN HIS WILL, I HOPE?

YES, MISTER BAJIN!

74 19-4

BAJIN COORTIN' HONEY PERZ! WHY, YON BLOKE'S MAIRRIT WI' FOWER WEE BOYS! I'M GOIN' OWER TAE HICKORY HOLLOW RIGHT NOO — I'LL SOON FIX HIM AN' HIS WENCHIN'...

MUCH OBLIGED, LOBEY!

LATER: AT HICKORY HOLLOW...

WAIT TILL YE SEE THIS — HE'LL NO' KEN WHAUR TAE LOOK WHEN I ASK HIM HOO HIS WIFE AN' WEANS ARE KEEPIN' THIS WEATHER!

THEY'VE GONE LOBEY! I'VE LOOKED ALL OVER!

HERE'S A WEE NOTE ON THE TABLE ADDRESSED TAE YE, VINEGAR...

DEAR UNCLE VINEGAR. MISTER BAJIN & ME HAS GONE TO GET MARRIED BY THE PREACHER AT GOOSEDUBS GULCH.
I SHALL ALWAYS THINK OF YOU BUT I LOVE MR BAJIN TOO ALTHOUGH HE IS THE BUNK ON THE BANJO. LOVE AND KISSES.
Honey Perz (Miss) xxxx

THEY'VE ELOPED

WE MUST GO AFTER THEM!

77 22-4

AT A TEA-ROOM IN GOOSEDUBS GULCH...

WELL, HERE WE ARE, HONEY! HAVE ANOTHER SCONE WHILE I GO AND FIX THINGS WITH THE PREACHER — BUT FIRST LET ME KISS YOU ON THE FOREHEAD ERE I TAKE OFF...

HOW GALLANT!

SPLASH

LATER...

RANK IS A LONG TIME A-COMIN' BACK — I DO TRUST NOTHING HAS HAPPENED TO THE DEAR MAN. MEANTIME I SHALL CONSUME ANOTHER BUN AND PERHAPS WIRE IN TO A PIE. AH, HERE HE IS — OR IS IT?

WHY, RANK, I SCARCELY KNEW YOU WEARING THAT STRANGE HEAD-GEAR! PRAY WHAT HAS HAPPENED TO YOUR NICE BLACK FEDORA — AND WHERE IS THE PREACHER?

THE PREACHER AND I ARE GOING TO HAMPDEN — HE WILL MARRY US ON MONDAY!

I WOULD GET MIXED UP IN A NUTTY STRIP LIKE THIS!

78 23-4

OKAY, BAJIN—LET'S HEAR YOUR REASON FOR BEIN' FREE T'MARRY HONEY IN SPITE O' THE FACT THAT YE'RE MAIRRIT ALREADY

BECAUSE I AM A MORMON! BRIGHAM YOUNG AND I WERE CHINAS BACK IN SALT LAKE CITY! I CAN HAVE UMPTEEN WIVES IF I WISH—THERE'S MY LICENCE

A MORMON! HE'S RIGHT! HERE'S HIS LICENCE SIGNED BY 'B. YOUNG (MR.)'

A CLEVER FORGERY, BUT GOOD ENOUGH FOR THESE OAFS!

PRAY PROCEED WITH THE CEREMONY, PREACHER

I DON'T CARE IF YO'RE BRIGHAM YOUNG HIMSELF. BAJIN—YO' AIN'T A-MARRYIN' HONEY—NOT WHILE I GOT BREATH IN ME BODY, SUH!

INDEED? AND WHAT WOULD A SAWED-OFF LITTLE RUNT LIKE YOU BE PREPARED TO DO ABOUT THE MATTER?

VINEGAR'S WEE BUT HE'S GEMME!

BONK!

81 27-4

YE'VE KNOCKED OOT BAJIN WI' THAT LUCKY PUNCH, VINEGAR! NOW'S WUR CHANCE TAE GET HONEY BACK TAE HICKORY HOLLOW—YOU TAKE HER FEET—C'MON!

OKAY!

LATER...

BAJIN'LL BE EFTER US WI' HIS THUGS SHORTLY BUT WE'RE NO' FAUR AFF THE CREEK NOO—HONEY'S COMIN' ROON'!

PERTICK?

RANK—WHERE'S MY RANK?

AW, SHUT UP ABOOT RANK! I'M SICK TIRED HEARIN' ABOOT THAT NYAFF!

SHE STILL LOVES HIM...

YERE NO' GOIN' BACK TAE HICKORY HOLLOW—YE'RE COMIN' HAME TAE MY HOOSE... BAJIN'LL NO' DARE COME NEAR THE PLACE

MUCH OBLIGED!

82 28-4

AT LOBEY'S HOUSE IN CALTON CREEK...

THERE! WE GOT HAME SAFE. JIST SIT DOON AN' I'LL MAKE YESE A WEE CUP O' TEA!

WAN WUMMAN'S MAIR TROUBLE THAN ALL TOFFY TEETH'S INJUNS PIT THEGITHER! HER AN' HER 'RANKIE' — I'LL 'RANKIE' HIM IF HE COMES NEAR THE PLACE. BUT VINEGAR WILL HIV TAE GET BACK TAE HIS RABBITS, AN' HONEY CANNAE STOP HERE ALONE- OH, DEARIE ME!

A VERY NICE TEA, LOBEY!

YE HIVNAE ETT NOTHIN'... YE AFF YIR CHUCK, HEN?

I THINK I SHALL RETIRE TO BED!

OKAY HONEY -THE WEE ROOM AT THE TOP O' THE LANDIN'- G'NIGHT AN' SWEET DREAMS

NICE CLEAN GOONIE

83 29-4

AS HONEY PREPARES FOR BED SOMETHING STIRS IN THE MOONLIGHT BEHIND A SHRUB IN LOBEY'S GARDEN...

ANIMAL, VEG, OR MINERAL ?

N LOBEY'S BEST BEDROOM HONEY SLUMBERS PEACEFULLY...

GLUG GLUG GLUG GLUG ZZZZZZZZZ

PUTT PUTT PUTT ZZZZZZZ

PSSST!

ZZZZZZZ

RANKIE!

HONEY! SHOVE ON SOME CLOTHES IN CASE YOU GET FLEE AND LET US 'FLU! MY HORSE IS BELOW SO KINDLY GET THE SKATES ON!

84 30-4

I CANNAE SLEEP FOR WORRYIN' ABOOT VINEGAR AN' HONEY PERZ — WISH I KENT WHIT TAE DAE FOR THE BEST. WHIT'S THAT — VOICES ON THE LANDIN'!

IT'S BAJIN AN' HONEY PERZ RUNNIN' AWA' AGAIN! THEY'RE GOIN' DOON THE LADDER TO HIS HORSE! I'VE GOT AN IDEA! BAJIN'S NO' THE ONLY WAN WI' NEFARIOUS PLANS!

ON THE LADDER...

NO ONE WILL PURSUE US THIS TIME — WE SHALL BE FAR AWAY BY THE TIME THEY RAISE THE HUE AND CRY!

HUE WHO?

AWFY DUMB

WE ARE ALMOST AT THE BOTTOM OF THE LADDER, HONEY — THEN WE SHALL JUMP ON MY TRUSTY STEED AND GALLOP OFF TO BE MARRIED! MY TRUSTY STEED IS 18 HANDS HIGH, HAS THE HEART OF A LION, AND A FACE LIKE A HORSE

85

THERE! WE HAVE SAFELY NEGOTIATED THE LADDER SO LET US NOW TODDLE SMARTLY ROUND THIS CORNER AND JUMP ON MY TRUSTY STEED...

I CANNOT BELIEVE MY HIGH-POWERED HYPNOTIC EYES! THAT IS MY SADDLE BUT IT IS DEFINITELY NOT MY TRUSTY STEED — UNLESS OF COURSE, IT HAS SHRUNK CONSIDERABLY WITH THE EARLY MORNING DEW...

SOOK
SOOK

YE'LL HIV TAE BE UP EARLIER IN THE MORNIN' TAE CATCH AULD LOBEY, BAJIN! THAT'S 'TOTTY', ELFIE'S WEE FOAL! I JIST SWITCHED YIR GEAR AN' PIT YOUR HORSE IN THE STABLE — SO WHAUR D'YE THINK YE'RE GOIN' NOO?

CURSES! FOILED AGAIN!

86

HONEY'S FENTIT

THE SOONER I HAVE A SHOW-DOWN WITH YOU THE BETTER, SHERIFF DOSSER! I AM THE FASTEST MAN ON THE DRAW IN THE 48 STATES. YOU'RE TIME HAS COME — I AM WAITING FOR YOU TO GO FOR YOUR GUN...

IS THAT SO, BAJIN? WELL, I'LL NO' TAKE YE AT A DISADVANTAGE, SO YOU GO FOR YOUR GUN WHEN YE'RE READY!

QUICK AS THE HEAD OF A STRIKING RATTLER, BAJIN'S HAND DARTS FOR HIS HOLSTER — HIS BLACK COLT FLASHES UPWARDS AND...

87

VISION IS TEMPORARILY OBSCURED BY A LARGE CLOUD OF CORDITE SMOKE

MA GRANNIE COULD SWALLY A PINT QUICKER THAN YOU CAN DRAW, BAJIN! C'MON HAME, HONEY...

HE PUT A BULLET DOWN THE BARREL OF MY SIX-GUN — INCREDIBLE!

WAIT! I ADMIT YOU BEAT ME TO THE DRAW THAT TIME, SHERIFF, BUT MY RIGHT ARM WAS NUMB FROM HUMPHING MISS PERZ DOWN THE LADDER — WE SHALL MEET AGAIN — GOOD DAY!

AWA' AN' BILE YIR CAN!

YOU SHOULDN'T BE RUDE TO RANKIE, MR DOSSER — HE'S NOT AS BLACK AS HE IS PAINTED...

FUMIN'

HE COULDNAE BE ONY BLACKER!

I WON'T HAVE YOU SAYING THESE THINGS ABOUT MY FIANCÉ — I INTEND TO MARRY HIM AND NOBODY IS GOING TO STOP ME!

WELL, YE'RE FORTY, HONEY, SO I SUPPOSE YOU CAN DAE WHIT YE LIKE — BUT YE'RE MAKIN' A BIG MISTAKE, SO YE ARE...

RIGHT IN THE HUFF, NOO

88

AT RANK BAJIN'S OFFICE...

THAT LOBEY DOSSER OAF MAY BE POPULAR WITH READERS OF THIS STRIP BUT HE IS A LARGE PAIN IN THE NECK TO MISTER & MISSUS BAJIN'S LITTLE BOY, RANK — YES, INDEED!

I HAVE MANY OLD SCORES TO SETTLE WITH L. DOSSER — THE MEDDLING FOOL HAS RUINED MY NEFARIOUS PLANS ONCE TOO OFTEN! HARK! THE 'PHONE!

THE BELL'S BROKE

CRASH.

CRASH

HULLO, RANKIE — HONEY SPEAKING! I'M 'PHONING FROM A BOX ...

YES, YES — WHAT'S ON YOUR MIND ...

AN ASIDE:

IF YOU HAVE ONE, WHICH I DOUBT!

COME FOR ME ON MONDAY EVENING AND WE SHALL BE MARRIED — I HAVE SPOKEN TO MR DOSSER AND TOLD HIM I HAVE MADE MY DECISION!

INDEED A MOST ATTRACTIVE PROPOSITION! I'LL BE AROUND FOR YOU MONDAY— GOOD BYE!

HEE-HEE-HEE! HICKORY HOLLOW AND THE PLUTONIUM ARE ALMOST IN MY CLUTCHES ...

89

WELL, THAT'S THAT: HONEY'S BEIN' MAIRRIT TAE BAJIN ON MONDAY UNLESS THERE'S A MIRACLE HAPPENS. I'M AWA DOON TAE MA OFFICE NOO, VINEGAR, SO CHEERIO!

IN

S'LONG, LOBEY! ...SIGH...

LATER: AT LOBEY'S OFFICE ...

IT'LL TAKE A MIRACLE TAE STOP THE MERRIAGE NOO, SO IT WULL — COME IN!

RAT TAT A TAT TAT

TAT TAT

SHERIFF

HOWDY, SHERIFF! I JUST GOT IN FROM SAN ANTONIO — BIN RIDIN' FOR DAYS NOW — THE NAME IS O'GOLD — HART O'GOLD — HOWDY, HOWDY!

WHAUR'S YIR STEWART GRAINGER NOO?

HOWDY! GOSH, BUT YE'RE A NICE-LOOKIN' BIG BLOKE!

THANKS, PODNER! AND I GOT SOME REAL URGENT BUSINESS TO DISCUSS WITH YA ...

HIV A PEW AN' GIE'S YIR CRACK, SONNY!

WHO IS THIS GEEZER WITH THE FANCY DIAL? HE HAS UPSET THE WHOLE STRIP ...

90

GOOD AFTERNOON, MY DEAR HONEY! I HAVE CALLED TO BE MARRIED TO YOU AS ARRANGED DURING OUR TELEPHONE CONVERSATION OF 6TH INST ...

MUCH OBLIGED!

JUST WASHED HER HERR

PERMIT ME TO SAY HOW SMASHING YOU LOOK! YOU'D CHARM THE BIRDS OFF THE TREES — OR ON SECOND THOUGHTS THEY'D BE MORE LIKELY TO DROP OFF DEAD ...

WHAT A PRETTY COMPLIMENT!

TUGGY BIT

BONE FAE THE NECK UP

HONEY AND I ARE NOW TODDLING SMARTLY OUT OF HERE TO BE WED, MISTER HILL — ARE YOU READY, HONEY?

KNOCK KNOCK

YES, RANKIE!

GOODBYE, HONEY! SNIFF ...

COME IN!

HULLO! THIS IS MY YOUNG FREEN' HART O'GOLD FAE SAN ANTONIO — MEET THE FOLKS, HART!

HOWDY!

SWOON

HONEY'S FENTIT

LANDSAKES! THE POOR GAL HAS FAINTED — HERE LET ME HELP HER TO HER FEET ...

STAND BACK, O'GOLD — SHE IS MINE!

A COLD GLINT COMES INTO HART'S STEADY GREY EYES ...

SMILE WHEN YA SAY THAT, STRANGER! A COLD GLINT HAS JUST COME INTO MY STEADY GREY EYES ..

THIS JERK IS NOBODY'S FOOL! I'LL SMOOTH THE MATTER OVER.

I WAS ONLY JOKING, MISTER O'GOLD — NO OFFENCE!

THAT'S BETTER! I WILL NOW LET THE COLD GLINT FADE FROM MY STEADY GREY EYES ... MISS PERZ HAS RECOVERED!

THUMP THUMP THUMP

HONEY'S HERT

92

WHEN YOU ARE READY, HONEY, LET US CHASE OFF OUT OF HERE AND BE WED — BUT QUICKLY, TOO!

I HAVE MADE CERTAIN ALTERATIONS IN MY PLANS IN LIGHT OF RECENT DEVELOPMENTS, MISTER BAJIN — OUR WEDDING IS CANCELLED! THANK YOU, MISTER O'GOLD, YOU MAY NOW ASSIST ME TO MY PINS!

IT APPEARS, MA'AM, THAT MISTER BAJIN HAS TAKEN UMBRAGE AT YOUR CANCELLATION OF THE WEDDING — HE HAS GONE OFF IN A FIT OF PIQUE

I'M SORRY TO HAVE TRAMPLED ON HIS HEART, MR O'GOLD — I'M JUST A LITTLE FLIRT, AREN'T I? TEE-HEE-HEE

SHE'S AWAY AGAIN

MEANTIME...

OH, TUSH! I SHALL GALLOP INTO THE HILLS FOR A WHILE AND THINK UP A NEFARIOUS PLAN TO RID MYSELF OF THIS HART O'GOLD LILY! IT IS STICKING OUT A MILE THAT HONEY HAS FALLEN FOR HIM! IT IS ALSO PERFECTLY OBVIOUS...

PERTICK?

IN THE HILLS I SHALL CAMP WITH MY NASTY CONFEDERATES AND WHILE AWAY MY TIME THINKING UP VILLAINOUS PLOTS!

FORWARD AT AN INCREASED PACE, HORSE, OR I SHALL HAVE YOU PAINTED BY MATISSE!

THE HORSE DAEIN' IT'S BEST TAE

WHEN I AM GOOD AND READY I SHALL RETURN TO HICKORY HOLLOW AND TAKE POSSESSION BY FOUL MEANS OR FOUL — BUT MEANTIME I AM DISAPPEARING FROM THIS STRIP FOR A WHILE ...

ABOUT TIME, TOO! WE'RE ALL SICK TIRED LOOKING AT YOU AND LISTENING TO YOU NATTERING AWAY TO YOURSELF. MAYBE WE'LL GET SOME ACTION NOW...

93

MY YOUNG FREEN' HART HERE IS A FORMER COOPUNCHER TURNT URANIUM PROSPECTOR HE THINKS THERE'S URANIUM ABOOT HERE SOMEWHERE, DON'T YE, SONNY?

I DO, SHERIFF—AND I INTEND TO START PROSPECTING IMMEDIATELY IN THIS DISTRICT

WELL, I DOOT YE'LL NO' FIN' ONY IN CALTON CREEK, BUT YE KIN HAE A BASH IF YE WANT TAE SO LONG AS YE'RE NO' GOIN' TAE DIG UP A' WUR STREETS...

NO NEED FOR THAT, SHERIFF! I HAVE HERE MY GEIGER COUNTER WHICH WILL INSTANTLY LOCATE ANY URANIUM DEPOSITS IN THE NEIGHBORHOOD

GREAT, EH? WHIT'LL THEY THINK O' NEXT!

WELL AWA' YE GO AN' GET STERTED, SONNY, AN' HONEY HERE'LL GO WI' YE AN' HELP YE TAE COONT YIR GEIGERS. I HOPE YE'RE LUCKY!

OKAY, SHERIFF, — S'LONG!

94

NOT A WORD OF THIS PLUTONIUM FIND TO ANYONE, MISS PERZ, OR WE SHALL BE MOBBED BY FOREIGN AGENTS AND OTHER BAD TYPES...

MY LIPS ARE SEALED, MISTER O'GOLD...

GOOD! WELL LET US NOW GIT ON BACK TO CALTON CREEK, MA'AM, AND TELL SHERIFF DOSSER OF OUR FIND — BUT WAIT!

?

WHAT IS THE MATTER NOW, MISTER O'GOLD? YOU HAVE DRAWN YOURSELF UP TO YOUR FULL HEIGHT AND A LOOK OF APPREHENSION IS REGISTERED ON YOUR LEAN, TANNED, BOYISH FACE...

I FEEL WE ARE BEING WATCHED — BUT LET US GO ANYWAY!

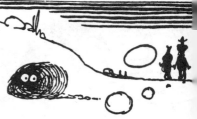

AS HART & HONEY RIDE OFF INTO THE SETTING SUN TWO SMOULDERING EYES STUDY THEM FROM A RABBIT BURROW

HOW MUCH DO YOU BET THE EYES AREN'T THOSE OF RID SKWERR, A SMALL FOREIGN AGENT WHO HAS BEEN SPECIALLY TRAINED TO LIVE IN RABBIT BURROWS?

97

THERE NOW! I HAVE BEEN IN TOUCH WITH THE STATE DEPARTMENT ON THE INGENIOUS TWO-WAY RADIO AND TELEVISION SET BUILT IN TO MY TOP DENTURES — THEY ARE SENDING A PLUTONIUM EXCAVATOR BY FAST 'PLANE RIGHT AWAY!

THE STATE DEPARTMENT HAS ALSO ASKED ME TO GIVE YOU THIS CHEQUE FOR $50,000, MISTER HILL — PERHAPS YOU'D LIKE TO GO BUY YOURSELF A YACHT AND SOME AUTOMOBILES WHILE I MAKE ARRANGEMENTS TO START WORK AT HICKORY HOLLOW...

MUCH OBLIGED

$50,000 WITH MORE TO COME, UNCLE VINEGAR! OH, HOW JOLLY! I CANNOT BELIEVE IT ... I SHALL GET MYSELF A NEW GOWN AND A QUARTER OF CHOCOLATE GINGERS RIGHT AWAY!

DEAR HART! HOW FINE AND GOOD HE IS, BUT HE NEVER SEEMS TO NOTICE POOR LITTLE ME ... SOB ... SNIFF ... PERHAPS, HOWEVER, HE WILL GIVE ME A TUMBLE NOW THAT I AM IN THE COIN ...

98

AT HICKORY HOLLOW...

WITH THIS EXCAVATOR WE ARE BRINGING UP TONS OF FINE PLUTONIUM AND ARE STORING IT IN THE BARN — BUT WE SHALL NEED A DAY AND NIGHT GUARD TO PREVENT PILFERING OF THE PRECIOUS SUBSTANCE..

I'LL STAY HERE AT NICHT AN' WATCH IT FOR YE, HART, SO YE'LL NO' NEED TAE WORRY YIR HEID ABOOT IT...

THANKS, PARDNER!

LATER ...

4:30 P.M. SHERIFF - I'M PUSHING OFF NOW IN ACCORDANCE WITH UNION REGULATIONS. YOU'LL BE OKAY HERE TILL MORNING?

AYE, SURE - GOOD NIGHT, SONNY...

AND LATER STILL — LOBEY SETTLES DOWN BESIDE THE PLUTONIUM IN THE OLD BARN...

KINNA SPOOKY IN HERE - BUT I'M NO' FEART - NO' MUCH, ONYWAY... WHIT WIS THAT CREAKIN'?

BEST PLUTON

99

THIS PLACE WID PIT THE BREEZE UP YE! THERE'S SOMETHIN' AHINT ME — I'LL PULL OOT MA GUN AN' TURN ROON' QUICK AS LIGHTNIN'...

BES PLUT

COME OOT O' THERE WHOEVER YE ARE OR I'LL FILL YE FU' O' LEED SLUGS!

B OPLU

BOSKI POSKIPOP?

OH-HO! MY, BUT YOU'RE A QUEER LOOKIN' WEE JOKER I MUST SAY! WHIT'S YIR NAME - AN' WHIT ARE YE DAEIN' IN AMONG WUR GUID PLUTONIUM MAY I ASK?

100

BOSKI POSKIPOP?

A FURRINER IF EVER I SEEN WAN - BUT HE LOOKS A HERMLESS ENOUGH WEE SOWL. HEY, WEE JOKER, SIT DOON AN' HAE A CUP O' TEA AN' YE CAN KEEP ME COMPANY TILL THE MORNIN'...

HIV ANOTHER PIECE O' MA CORN MEAT SANGWICH, WEE JOKER, AN' SOME MAIR CHAR. WIRE IN— THAT'S THE WEE MAN! CAN YE SPEAK ENGLISH?

BOSKI POSKIPOP? YUM, YUM, YUM...

HE CAN CERTAINLY GET TORE IN TAE THE CHUCK. YE'D THINK HE'D NEVER SEEN A BITE! IT'S ABOOT NINE O'CLOCK IN THE MORNIN' SO HART SHOULD BE HERE SOON... THIS WILL BE HIM NOO...

YUM YUM GLUG

HULLO, HART—THIS IS A WEE JOKER I FUN' CREEPIN' ABOOT IN THE BARN LAST NIGHT— HE CANNAE SPEAK ENGLISH...

MY KNOWLEDGE OF EUROPEAN LANGUAGES WILL BE HELPFUL THEN — I SHALL QUESTION HIM RIGHT AWAY...

LATER...

IT TRANSPIRES THAT THIS CHARACTER IS A SPY IN THE EMPLOY OF A FOREIGN POWER BUT HE IS CHEESED OFF WITH LIVING IN RABBIT BURROWS AND WISHES TO WORK WITH YOU BECAUSE YOU HAVE BEEN GOOD TO HIM — HIS NAME IS RID SKWERR

PLEASED TAE MEET YE, RID!

101

THAT WEE JOKER, RID SKWERR, FOLLOWS ME ABOOT LIKE A WEE DUG - HE CLEANS MA GUNS, BRUSHES MA BITTS, MAKES THE DINNER AN' WASHES MA SHIRTS. I'VE LEARNT HIM A FEW WORDS O' ENGLISH TAE. HEY, RID! C'MERE A WEE MEENIT!

BOSKI POSKIPOP?

AYE, THAT'S RIGHT! NOO, I WANT YE TAE TELL MISTER O'GOLD HERE THE ENGLISH I LEARNT YE THIS MORNIN'...

BOSKI POSKIPOP?

NAW, NAW, NAW! NO' "BOSKI POSKIPOP" — WHIT DID I LEARN YE THIS MORNIN', RID? COME ON, NOO, DON'T BE SHY- YE'RE AMANG FREEN'S ...

GUID AULD RANGERS!

NOO IS THAT NO' GREAT FOR WAN LESSON!

102

MY WORK HYAR IS ALMOST FINISHED - I HAVE EXCAVATED EVERY PARTICLE OF PLUTONIUM! ALL THET REMAINS TUH BE DONE NOW IS TO ARRANGE FOR ITS TRANSPORTATION TUH THE SECRET ATOMIC PILE AT 1374 15ᵗʰ AVENOO, WASHINGTON, D.C., TWO UP, KNOCK TWICE AND ASK FOR HARRY...

SO EXCUSE ME WHILE I FIX THINGS WITH WASHINGTON ON MY CUNNING TWO-WAY RADIO BUILT IN TUH MY TOP DENTURES ... WHEEE-EE ... BUZZ-ZZZZ ...

HULLO, WASHINGTON! O'GOLD HERE! SEND 'PLANE FDR PLUTONIUM RIGHT AWAY ... OVER!

OKAY, OGOLD! LEAVING TONIGHT.- OVER!

NOO THAT YIR WORK'S DONE, HART, ARE YE GOIN' AWA' TAE LEAVE US?

YES, SHERIFF- I'LL GO BACK TUH WASHINGTON IN THE 'PLANE WITH THE PLUTONIUM! WOULD YUH LIKE TUH COME ALONG FOR THE TRIP WITH RID SKWERR?

103

BY GOLLY- BUT THAT'S AN IDEA! YE WIDNAE BE FLEEIN' OWER ST. LOUIS WID YE? THE SCOTTISH TOURIN' TEAM'S PLAYIN' THERE ON WEDNESDAY AN' I WIDNAE MIND GIEIN' THEM A BIT HAMPDEN ROAR TAE CHEER THEM UP...

THAT MIGHT BE ARRANGED, SHERIFF!

AS THE DAWN STREAKS THE EASTERN SKYLINE, A BIG AIR-FREIGHTER ROARS DOWN ON HICKORY HOLLOW...

THE BUSINESS OF LOADING THE PLUTONIUM GOES ON ALL MORNING...

ANOTHER FORTY SACKS, AL, AND WE'RE THROUGH!

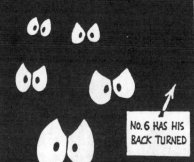

HIDDEN IN THE TAIL OF THE 'PLANE ARE SIX DESPERATE FOREIGN AGENTS WHO CLIMBED ABOARD IN WASHINGTON UNDER COVER OF DARKNESS. THEY ARE UP TO NO GOOD, I CAN TELL YOU...

NO. 6 HAS HIS BACK TURNED

... AND HIDDEN IN THE NOSE OF THE 'PLANE, DISGUISED AS A SACK OF PLUTONIUM, IS HONEY PERZ. HONEY IS DETERMINED TO GO WITH HART & LOBEY, BUT HART HAS REFUSED TO TAKE HER WITH THEM— HENCE HER STOWING AWAY...

BEST PLUTONIUM

PERHAPS I OUGHT TO HAVE TOLD YOU ALL THIS BEFORE, BUT IT SLIPPED MY MIND.

TOO LATE DOES LOBEY REALISE THAT FOUR OF THE DESPERATE FOREIGN AGENTS ARE WAITING FOR HIM IN AMBUSH...

BAM! GRUNT! WOOSH!

THE CUPBOARD ALSO HIM INTO PUT, BORIS - WE HAVE NOTHING MORE TO FEAR FROM THEM! 'THE BRAIN' WILL REWARD US WELL FOR THIS DAY'S WORK WHEN WE TOUCH DOWN TOMORROW IN THE FATHERLAND...

JA, JA, JA COMMISSAR

STEADILY HEADING NORTH, THE BIG AIR FREIGHTER APPROACHES THE ARCTIC CIRCLE...

ARCTIC CIRCLE

BIG AIR FREIGHTER

SNAW

109

IN THE PILOT'S CABIN...

IT WAS QUITE A JOB THROWING THE REGULAR PILOT & NAVIGATOR OUT OF THAT SMALL WINDOW, VLADIMIR - BUT ANYTHING FOR THE FATHERLAND! THE COMMISSAR & THE BOYS HAVE DISPOSED OF THE OTHERS - SOON WE SHALL BE HOME WITH THE PRECIOUS PLUTONIUM - 'THE BRAIN' WILL BE WAITING...

...

IN THE CUPBOARD, LOBEY, HART, & RID SKWERR SOON RECOVER FROM THE DUNTS ADMINISTERED TO THEIR RESPECTIVE SKULLS by THE DESPERATE FOREIGN AGENTS, BUT...

THE STEEL DOOR'S LOCKED! WE CANNAE GET OOT!

WE SHORE ARE IN A FIX NOW, SHERIFF! THESE THUGS HAVE CLEVERLY KIDNAPPED US AND STOLEN THE PLUTONIUM. IF THEY SUCCEED IN THEIR MISSION IT MEANS WAR!

NAW!

BUT AYE!

WE JES' GOTTA GIT OUTA HERE, SO STAND BACK WHILE I BLAST THE LOCK OFF...

WAIT, HART! LISTEN — SOMEBODY AT THE DOOR TURNIN' THE KEY!

110

SLOWLY & SILENTLY THE DOOR SWINGS OPEN AND A BLACK SHADOW FALLS ON THE THREE FRIENDS...

CURR-ASH!

OUCH!

QUITE MYSTERIOUS THE WHOLE AFFAIR IS IT NOT?

WHO'S THAT? COME WAN STEP NEARER AN' I'LL GIE YE THE WORKS!

WE'LL FIGHT TO THE DEATH, SHERIFF — STAND BACK, BY HEAVENS!

HEROIC JOKER IS HART

A DULCET VOICE SPEAKS THROUGH THE GLOOM of THE CUPBOARD...

FOLLOW ME— AND KEEP QUIET...

WHOEVER IT WAS HAS SKEDADDLED! NAW· THERE'S SOMEBODY BECKONIN' US — COME ON...

.I. WIGGLE · WIGGLE

/11

JUST SO AS YOU'LL SLEEP TONIGHT I'LL TELL YOU THAT THE MYSTERIOUS CHARACTER WITH THE BECKONING FOREFINGER IS NONE OTHER THAN HONEY PERZ WHO, OBSERVING THE PLIGHT OF HER FRIENDS, CREPT DOWN THE CORRIDOR AND UNLOCKED THE DOOR ...

THE REASON FOR HER NOT IMMEDIATELY REVEALING HER IDENTITY IS BECAUSE HER NEB IS SOMEWHAT SHINY THRO' HER BEING SO LONG IN THE PLUTONIUM SACK AND SHE WANTS TO GET THE GLAMOUR ON BEFORE SHE MEETS MISTER O'GOLD. ANY QUESTIONS?

THIS STRIP IS A POOR VEHICLE FOR MY TALENTS. IT LACKS CONTINUITY, ACTION, & INTEREST AND IS QUITE OBVIOUSLY DRAWN BY A HAM — BUT YESTERDAY'S PREMATURE REVELATION OF THE IDENTITY OF OUR RESCUER WAS THE LAST STRAW — I QUIT!

OH, THE CHEEK!

NOW, NOW, HART!

I'M SERIOUS, SHERIFF!

WELL, YE CANNAE QUIT HERE FLEEIN' ABOOT IN AN AIRY-PLANE FU' O' DESPERATE FURRIN' AGENTS — SO LET'S CAIRRY ON FAE YESTERDAY'S STRIP STERTIN' WI' ME SAYIN' 'THANKS FOR RESCUIN' US, HONEY'...

OH, WELL— ALL RIGHT!

THANKS FOR RESCUIN' US, HONEY ...

A PLEASURE, I'M SURE...

/112

NOO LISTEN ... I'M GONNAE MAKE A BIG HOLE IN THE PETROL TANK WI' THIS DRILL...

I GET IT, SHERIFF! THEN THE SIX DESPERATE FOREIGN AGENTS'LL BE FORCED TUH LAND?

EXAC'LY!

INSIDE THE 'PLANE... NAE SIGNS O' ONYBODY RESCUIN' US! DOOT WE MUST HIV LANDED MILES FAE CEEVILIZATION...

HELP!

HERE'S SOMEBODY NOW! TWO HUSKY HUNTERS

DON'T WORRY IN THAR! ZEKE AN' ME'LL CUT OUR WAY THRO' TO YA WITH OUR HUNTIN' KNIVES— WE'LL HAVE YA OUT IN TWO TICKS...

TWO TICKS LATER...

THAR Y'ARE STRANGERS! WELCOME TO THE YUKON...

THANKS 'N HOWDY! WHERE'S THE NEAREST TOWN, PLEASE?

WAAL, LEMME SEE, NOW...

/15

RECKON WOLF'S CLAW IS 'BOUT NEAREST, STRANGER— IT'S TWO DAYS DOWN RIVER FROM HERE, BUT THE PORCUPINE'S FROZE OVER SO IT LOOKS LIKE YOU'LL HAVE TO STOP WITH RUBE AN' ME AT OUR LOG CABIN IN THE ROCKIES TILL SPRING...

'IN THE ROCKIES'! PAY NO ATTENTION TO ZEKE— HE USED TO PLAY KAZOO FOR BIG BILL CAMPBELL AND HIS GEOGRAPHY IS THE BUNK...

WAAL, THAT'S MIGHTY BIG OF YOU BOYS OFFERIN' TO PUT US UP UNTIL SPRING— BUT I ALMOST FORGOT! THE PLUTONIUM AND THE DESPERATE FOREIGN AGENTS! ...PARDON ME WHILE I SEARCH THE WRECKAGE!

TEN MINUTES LATER...

THE PLUTONIUM IS INTACT, BUT THE DESPERATE FOREIGN AGENTS HAVE GONE! THEY MUST HAVE FLED INTO THE HILLS WHILE WE WERE TRAPPED IN THE WRECKAGE...

HOW SAD!

WAAL, LET'S GIT, FRIENDS— OUR CABIN IS JUST OVER THIS RIDGE, SO YOU'LL BE ABLE TO KEEP AN EYE ON THE 'PLANE FROM THAR...

HOW HANDY!

/16

IMAGINE HIVIN' TAE STEY HERE TILL SPRING! THE FOLKS IN CALTON CREEK'LL THINK I'M DEID— AN' PUIR AULD ELFIE... OH, DEARIE ME... NEVER EVEN SEEN THE ST. LOUIS GEMME, NEITHER...

THAR'S THE CABIN OVER THAR, FRIENDS!

MUCH OBLIGED!

"IS THIS NO' CANADA WE'RE IN NOO, ZEKE?"

IT IS!

WELL, HOO FAUR ARE YE FAE TORONTO? THERE'S A GEMME ON THERE THE NIGHT...

ABOUT 3500 MILES...

OWER FAUR... I WIDNAE GET HAME, NAW...

WELCOME TO OUR HUMBLE HOME, FOLKS! NOW I'LL RUSTLE UP SOME PORK & BEANS...

WELL, WELL— LOOK WHO'S HERE!

THEM TWO CHARACTERS COME UP HERE PROSPECTIN' A MONTH AGO. NO LUCK— SO RUBE AN' ME GIVES 'EM A JOB MAKIN' UP SANDWICHES FER US TO TAKE WITH US ON OUR HUNTIN' TRIPS...

HOW SWEET OF YOU!

117

THAT'S ALL THEY DO — MAKE UP SANDWICHES FOR RUBE AN' ME...

YEAH... WE'RE ON PIECE WORK

MIGHTY FINE!

I'M A-GOIN' OVER TO TAKE A LOOK AT THE 'PLANE, SHERIFF — IT MAY NOT BE AS BADLY KNOCKED UP AS WE IMAGINE ...

OKAY, HART— I'LL COME WI' YE...

AN HOUR LATER...

FINE! THE PORT MOTOR IS ONLY SLIGHTLY DAMAGED AND THE STARBOARD WING IS BENT... BUT WITH MY GREAT MECHANICAL KNOWLEDGE I'LL HAVE THIS BIG AIR FREIGHTER AS GOOD AS NEW BY SATURDAV...

YE'RE A GENIUS, HART— NAE KIDDIN'!

HERE'S THE TWO HUSKY HUNTERS WI SOMETHIN' THEY'VE SHOT! WHIT KIND O' A BAIST'S _THAT_, HUSKY HUNTERS?

IT'S A BAAR, FOLKS... A GRIZZLY BAAR.

118

IT'S A HECK OF A LOOKIN' BEAR ...

WE KNOW... BUT NEILL CANNAE DRAW BEARS ...

YOU MEAN 'NEILL CANNAE DRAW, PERIOD'...

MIGHTY FINE!

THE 'PLANE IS TICKING OVER! ZEKE GAVE US A FEW GALLONS OF GAS TO GET US TO WASHINGTON SO WE WILL LEAVE AT DAWN TOMORROW, SHERIFF...

THAT'S GREAT, HART!

STICK 'EM UP AND DON'T TURN ROUND! INTO THE 'PLANE, BOYS, GET AND TAKE OFF - QUICKLY!

YUS!

ROAR... ROAR...

AS THE BIG AIR FREIGHTER ROLLS OFF, LOBEY DASHES IN PURSUIT...

COME BACK, SHERIFF! YOU'LL BE KILLED!

OH, YEAH?

MADE IT! JIST AN' NAE MAIR...

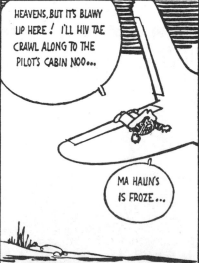

HEAVENS, BUT IT'S BLAWY UP HERE! I'LL HIV TAE CRAWL ALONG TO THE PILOT'S CABIN NOO...

MA HAUN'S IS FROZE...

HANGING ON GRIMLY, THE DIMINUTIVE SHERIFF CRAWLS SLOWLY ALONG THE FUSELAGE AS THE BIG AIR FREIGHTER ZOOMS OFF NORTH...

CHITTER CHITTER

IN THE PILOT'S CABIN...

A MOST SUCCESSFUL MISSION! WE HAVE THE PLUTONIUM INTACT! PUT THE BOOT DOWN BORIS AND WE WILL BE IN THE FATHERLAND TOMORROW. 'THE BRAIN' WILL BE PLEASED!

GOOD TIME WE ARE MAKING, COMMISSAR ... WE ARE NOW OVER THE BERING SEA!

FINE!

GIT YIR HAUN'S UP OR I'LL BLAW YIR BLINKIN' HEIDS AFF!

MERCY!

NOO GET OOT THE DOOR AN' INTAE THE WEE CUPBOARD — I'LL LOCK YESE IN AN' THAT'LL KEEP YESE OOT O' MISCHIEF ... HURRY ALONG NOO, PLEASE!

123

FIVE MINUTES LATER ...

WELL, THAT'S THEM A' LOCKED IN THE CUPBOARD, THE BAD RASCALS! IF THEY THOUGHT I WAS FEART FOR SIX AULD DESPERATE FURRIN' AGENTS. THEY'VE GOT ANITHER THINK COMIN'! WUNNER HOO YE FLEE THIS THING...

PILOT

THERE'S MAIR DIALS HERE THAN THERE ARE AT THE HILLINGTON CLOCK WORKS, BUT HERE'S A WEE BOOK ABOOT "HOO TAE FLEE AN' AIRYPLANE" ... "PIT THE LEFT KNOB IN AN' PULL THE RIGHT KNOB OOT, PIT THE LEFT KNOB IN AN' TURN IT ROON' ABOOT" ... SOUNDS LIKE THE 'COKEY-COKEY' ...

PILOT'S

AH, HERE'S A ROAD MAP! IF I KEEP TAE THE MAIN ROAD I CANNAE GO WRONG FOR WASHINGTON ...

SOME TIME LATER ...

NICE WEE TOON, WINNIPEG ... NOO FOR DETROIT!

GEE, MOITLE, WHAT FLYIN'!

124

CHOCK-A-BLOCK WI' MOTOR CAURS, DETROIT ... HO-HO-HO, I GIE'D THAT BLOKE ON THE BIKE A FRIGHT THE NOO ... HE'S FELL AFF ... NEXT STOP WASHINGTON!

PILOT

WASHINGTON, D.C.

HERE WE ARE! I'LL JIST LAND OOTSIDE THE TREASURY DEPARTMENT AN' GET SOMEBODY TAE HUMPH IN THE PLUTONIUM.   OOT THE ROAD, YOU WI' THE LUM HAT ... HONESTLY, THAE PEDESTRIANS!

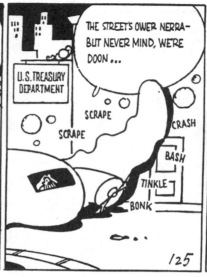

U.S. TREASURY DEPARTMENT

THE STREET'S OWER NERRA— BUT NEVER MIND, WE'RE DOON ...

SCRAPE

SCRAPE

CRASH

BASH

TINKLE

BONK

125

HULLO, MAC! MY NAME'S DOSSER, SHERIFF O' CALTON CREEK. I'VE A LOT O' PLUTONIUM FOR YE AN' SIX DESPERATE FURRIN' AGENTS LOCKED UP IN A WEE CUPBOARD

GEE, THAT'S GREAT! I'LL TELL THE F.B.I. RIGHT AWAY!

TREASURY DEPT

$1000

YOU HAVE OINED DE UNDYIN' GRATITUDE OF DEM GREAT UNITED STATES, SHERIFF, BY SAFELY DELIVERIN' DIS WUNNERFUL PLUTONIUM AN' ARRESTIN' DEM JOIKS OF FOREIGN AGENTS. DE COMMITTEE ON UN-AMERICAN ACTIVITIES IS PROUD OF YA, SO HELP YASELF TO A MEDAL ... TAKE TWO ...

DISTRICT ATTORNEY

MEDALS (ASSORTED)

DEM HOODLUMS IS DOWN IN DE CELLAR GETTIN' DE THOID DEGREE, SO POIDON ME WHILE I GET DE VICE SQUAD ON DE BLOWER ... HULLO, JOE · HAVE DEM JOIKS SQUEALED YET?

NOPE, BOSS! DEY JUST KEEP TALKIN' ABOUT 'DE BRAIN' AN' SINGIN' 'OL' MAN RIVER' ...

WHO'S DIS 'DE BRAIN' PUNK, SHERIFF? SOUNDS LIKE A FRENCHMAN TO ME ...

CANNAE TELL YE FOR CERTAIN, D.A.— BUT I'VE BEEN DAEIN' A BIT O' FIGURIN' AN' I THINK I'M ON HIS TRAIL ...

I'M GOIN' BACK TAE THE YUKON THE MORRA'— IF I CATCH UP WI' 'THE BRAIN' I'LL LET YE KNOW ...

GEE, DAT'S SOOPA-DOOPA! HERE, LET ME WRAP YOU UP SOME MORE MEDALS IN A BROWN-PAPER POICEL ...

WHO IS 'THE BRAIN'? WILL LOBEY CATCH HIM? LOOK OUT FOR A FURTHER BREATH-TAKING INSTALMENT OF THIS RED-BLOODED ACTION SERIAL ON MONDAY...

126

AT THE CABIN IN THE YUKON...

'AND THEN THE KIND FAIRY TURNED LITTLE CINDERELLA INTO A BEE-YOOT-I-FUL PRINCESS AND SHE AND THE PRINCE LIVED HAPPILY EVER AFTER ... THE END ' ... SIGH ...

FAIRY STORIES

OH, HOW I WISH SOME KIND FAIRY WOULD TURN ME INTO A BEAUTIFUL PRINCESS THEN MISTER O'GOLD WOULD FIND ME PRACTICALLY IRRESISTIBLE I HOPE...

MY NAME IS FAIRY NUFF! WITH THIS 'ERE MAGIC WAND I CAN MAKE YOU A SMASHER IN TWO TICKS...

FLASH

BANG

OH, GOODY GOODY GOODY!

127

I WILL NOW TAP YOU LIGHTLY ON THE CRUST LIKE SO... NOTHING HAS HAPPENED... I WILL TRY AGAIN... THERE... STILL NOTHING HAS HAPPENED... OH, FIE, BUT THESE UTILITY WANDS REALLY ARE THE BUNK... YOU MUST WAIT UNTIL I FIX THE THING, MY DEAR...

MUCH OBLIGED!

GOOD MORNING, MISTER O'GOLD! THIS IS FAIRY NUFF WHO IS GOING TO MAKE ME BEAUTIFUL WITH HER MAGIC WAND AND IS THERE ANY WORD OF MISTER DOSSER?

HOWDY, MISS NUFF! NO THERE IS NO WORD OF THE SHERIFF ... BUT, HARK... HERE IS A 'PLANE NOW!

A TINY AIRCRAFT COMES IN TO LAND AT THE LOG CABIN ...

IT'S MISTER BAJIN!

128

NEFARIOUS GREETINGS TO YOU! WHEN I RETURNED TO CALTON CREEK FROM MY HIDEOUT IN THE HILLS AND FOUND HICKORY HOLLOW DESERTED & THE PLUTONIUM GONE, I DECIDED TO TAKE A HOLIDAY IN THE YUKON WITH MY ILL-GOTTEN GAINS. STRANGE I SHOULD RUN INTO YOU LIKE THIS...

HARK, ANOTHER 'PLANE!

MR O'GOLD WILL NEVER LOOK AT ME NOW... NOT WITH THIS ENLARGED NEB... SOB SOB SNIFF...

IT'S MAYBE FOR THE BEST, HONEY... COME ON' WI' ME A MEENIT...

HULLO, EVERYBODY... THE PLANE'S COMIN' FOR US THE MORRA, BUT BEFORE IT ARRIVES I'VE SOMETHIN' TAE DAE...

AND WHAT IS THAT, PRAY?

ACCUSE YE O' BEIN' THE HEID O' A GANG O' DESPERATE FURRIN' AGENTS AN' FOR TRYIN TAE GET THE PLUTONIUM OOT O' THE COUNTRY... STICK 'EM UP, O'GOLD, YE'RE UNDER ARREST!

HONEY'S FENTIT

131

BUT YOU CAN'T DO THAT, DOSSER! HE IS THE HERO OF THIS STRIP ... I AM THE VILLAIN!

HAUD YIR TONGUE, BAJIN! WHO'S THE SHERIFF, YOU OR ME? COME ON, O'GOLD, TILL I LOCK YE UP, YE BAD CHARACTER...

WELL, HERE'S THE 'PLANE TAE TAK US HAME... IN YE GET EVERYBODY... S'LONG, HUSKY HUNTERS AN' THANKS... YE CAN KEEP THAE TWO WEE AIRYPLANES... O'GOLD WILL GO BACK TAE WASHINGTON WHAUR THE F.B.I. WILL DEAL WI' HIM.

WE'LL SOON BE HAME NOO... DON'T WORRY ABOOT YIR NEB, HEN... MINE WUS BIGGER THAN THAT THE TIME I GOT STUNG WI' A BEE...

TERRIBLE THING THAT ABOOT O'GOLD, THOUGH... HOODWINKIN' US A' THE TIME... JIST SHOWS YE... NEVER TRUST A BLOKE WI' A FANCY DIAL, AS MA MITHER USED TAE SAY... TERRIBLE BUSINESS RIGHT ENOUGH, AYE, TUT, TUT, TUT...

132

HE'S WORSE THAN YOU, BAJIN... A BIGGER VILLAIN THAN YOU EVER WUS...

I TAKE THAT AS AN INSULT TO MY PROFESSIONAL ABILITY, DOSSER, BUT NO MATTER- BELOW LIES CALTON CREEK AND MORE NEFARIOUS PLANS

HAME!

MUCH OBLIGED!

... The End ...

EXPLANATORY NOTE
— ◇ —
BEING THE LEAST LIKELY SUSPECT, HART O'GOLD WAS A NATURAL TO TAKE THE CAN BACK AS 'THE BRAIN'... THIS IS WHAT IS KNOWN AS A 'SURPRISE ENDING' ...JUST LIKE THE MOVIES, EH?
— ◇ —

LOBEY DOSSER
BY BUD NEILL
The Indian War

Note: Rid Skwerr is now employed by the Calton Creek Council to haunt the graveyard...

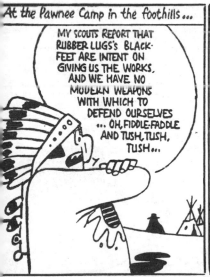

At the Pawnee Camp in the foothills...

Later...

Toffy Teeth, slightly incapacitated by a bullet hole through the back of his nut, struggles to his feet...

WHERE AM I — AND, WHAT IS MORE IMPORTANT, WHERE IS MY 50 MILLION BUCKS?

RANK!

MR BAJIN TOOK OFF A MINUTE AGO, CHIEF, WITH A LARGE SACKFUL OF UNCLE SAM'S CURRENCY...

WELL, WOULD YA CREDIT THAT, THE DOUBLE CROSSER!

DECAMPED WITH THE DIBS, EH? I HAVE ALWAYS SUSPECTED THAT BAJIN HIDES A BLACK SOUL UNDER A VENEER OF RESPECTABILITY

YUS, CHIEF

205

BUT OF COURSE THERE WOULD BE NO USE OF SAYING THAT TO HIM — ABOUT THE VENEER, I MEAN

NO, CHIEF

IT WOULD JUST GO IN VENEER AND OUT THE OTHER

MIGHTY FINE!

Arrayed in battle formation above the Pawnee camp, Rubber Lugs's Blackfeet await the signal to attack...

GET READY, GET SET...

The hills become alive with galloping Blackfeet, their single-shot rifles single-shooting like anything...

BANG! BANG! KIKI GO!

THESE TREACHEROUS BLACKFEET HAVE ATTACKED US DURING OUR LUNCH HOUR! TO YOUR POSTS, BRAVES, WITH YOUR REPEATING RIFLES! NO QUARTER! NO HALVES! NOT EVEN A FIVE-EIGHTHS

A vicious battle takes place, but it soon becomes apparent that the superior fire-power of the Pawnees is taking heavy toll of the attackers

WE REALLY LET OURSELVES IN FOR SOMETHING HERE, CHIEF! ANOTHER 5 MINUTES OF THIS AND WE'LL BE EXTINCT!

TELL MY BRAVES TO WITHDRAW TO THE HILLS — WE HAVE NO CHANCE AGAINST THESE REPEATING RIFLES... RUBBER LUGS HAS SPOKE!

HIM AGAIN

YOU PICK THE BULLETS OUTA ME, HAWK NOSE, THEN I'LL PICK 'EM OUTA YOU!

WE'LL GET A GOOD FEW BUCKS FOR THE LEAD!

206

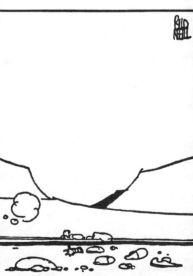

ON TOP OF THE THE TERRIBLE PRECIPICE (SEE MONDAY)

HULLO, TOFFY TEETH ! HOW ARE YOU, OLD CHAP. AND I HOPE YOUR MOTHER IS KEEPING BETTER ...

DON'T GIMME THAT STUFF, YOU CHEAP CROOK !

ATTA BOY. TOFFY !

FORK OUT MY 50,000,000 BUCKS OR I'LL TAKE IT OUT OF YOUR HIDE, AND MAYBE YOUR JEKYLL TOO ...

AWAY AND TAKE A RUNNING JUMP TO YOURSELF, AS DAVE WILLIS SAYS

SPRINGING LIKE A PANTHER, TOFFY TEETH IS AT RANK BAJIN'S THROAT ...

219

NOBODY HAS EVER SEEN YOUR FACE, BAJIN - BUT I AM GOING TO REMOVE YOUR HOOD !

NO ! NO ! NO !.

BAGS OF ACTION, EH ?

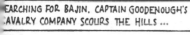

SEARCHING FOR BAJIN, CAPTAIN GOODENOUGH'S CAVALRY COMPANY SCOURS THE HILLS ...

HALT ! LEAVE US EXPLORE THIS ROCKY GORGE, MEN. AND, PRAY, WHAT IS THAT OBJECT LYING THERE ?

220

IT'S THE SHERIFF'S HORSE - SHOT DEAD !

RUBBER LUGS'S POSSE, IN PURSUIT OF RANK BAJIN COME TO A STRETCH OF THE NEW RAILROAD...

WE'LL RIDE ALONG THE TRACKS A LITTLE WAY THEN HEAD EAST – COME ON!

OKAY, CHIEF!

LATER ...

IT'S SHERIFF DOSSER! HE HAS BEEN KILLED BY A TRAIN!

LOOK, HE WAS TIED TO THE TRACK! IT'S MURDER!

221

IF THIS WAS BAJIN'S WORK, HEAVEN HELP HIM! ALL WE CAN DO, MEN, IS BURY THE REMAINS HERE AND RETURN TO CALTON CREEK WITH THE SAD NEWS...

CUT TO RIBBONS

TOFFY TEETH AND RANK BAJIN ARE LOCKED IN MORTAL COMBAT ON THE EDGE OF THE TERRIBLE PRECIPICE ...

BASH!

THUMP!

NOW, LET'S SEE WHAT YOU LOOK LIKE WITH YOUR HOOD OFF, YOU TWO-TIMING, DOUBLE-CROSSING THIEF!

RIP!

EEEEEEE!.

222

NO! NO! NO!

NO MAN HAS EVER LOOKED ON MY FACE AND REMAINED SANE!

GETTING PROPER GRUESOME THIS, AIN'T IT?

AT THE CREEK...

I HAVE SAD NEWS FOR YOU... WE FOUND... WE FOUND THE SHERIFF... A TRAIN GOT HIM, BUT HE HAD BEEN TIED TO THE RAILS — IT WAS MURDER!

NO' LOBEY!

LOBEY!

WE BURIED HIM AT THE SIDE OF THE TRACK... THERE WASN'T MUCH LEFT... THE VULTURES

CANNAE BELIEVE IT!

OOR LOBEY!

ONY IDEA WHO DONE IT?

NONE AT ALL

I REMOVED THE SLUGS FROM THE HORSE'S BODY... .38s NICKEL ... KNOW ANYBODY WHO TOTES A .38?

BAJIN USES A .38!

TOFFY TEETH DASHED ON THE JAGGED ROCKS BELOW... HE WON'T TALK AGAIN ... I WILL NOW REPLACE MY HOOD AND SCRAM TO THE MOUNTAINS! HEE·HEE·HEE!

LATER...

THERE! I AM MORE LIKE MYSELF NOW - PROCEED QUICKLY, HORSE!

CAREERING MADLY DOWN THE STEEP MOUNTAINSIDE, BAJIN'S GUN IS JOLTED FROM THE HOLSTER...

RID SKWERR, SORROWING FOR HIS FRIEND. LOBEY, ROAMS THE HILLS...

?

IN CALTON CREEK...

WHIT D'YE THINK O' THINGS NOO, THEN? ...'THE WELFARE STATE'... HUGHIE SAYS 'THE FAREWELL STATE' WID BE MAIR LIKER IT... HERE WEE RID COMIN'...

SO IT IS!

HULLO, RID! I'VE A WEE DRAP TEA AN' SUGAR FOR YE IF YE COME UP TAE THE HOOSE

FUN' A GUN!

THAT'S BAJIN'S GUN!

COME ON WE'LL GIE IT TAE CAPTAIN GOODENOUGH!

SOME HOURS LATER...

MY BALLISTICS EXPERT HAS FOUND THAT THE SHELLS WHICH KILLED EL FIDELDO WERE FIRED FROM THIS GUN! RANK BAJIN IS THE MURDERER!

WHIT DID I TELL YE...

SEE!

Panel 1: AT BAJIN'S HIDEOUT IN THE HILLS

LIKE ALL GOOD MURDERERS I HAVE A YEN TO REVISIT THE SCENE OF MY CRIME AND I SHALL DO SO RIGHT AWAY...

AGATHA CHRISTIE

Panel 2: LATER THAT DAY RID SKWERR IS WALKING ALONG THE RAIL-ROAD IN SEARCH OF FURTHER EVIDENCE...

BUD NEILL

Panel 3: BAJIN!

23₁

Panel 4: SMALL AND UNARMED THO' HE IS, RID SKWERR DETERMINES TO GET THE KILLER OF HIS FRIEND, LOBEY...

EUREKA! MY DASTARDLY PLAN SUCCEEDED! HIS FRIENDS HAVE BURIED HIM AT THE RAILSIDE... THAT'S THE END OF DOSSER, AND GOOD RIDDANCE, TOO!

Panel 5: AT CAPTAIN GOODENOUGH'S H.Q. IN CALTON CREEK...

WE MUST GET BAJIN DEAD OR ALIVE! OLD JAKE PRINGLE FOUND TOFFY TEETH'S BODY IN WILD HORSE GULCH THIS MORNING, SMASHED TO BITS ...THERE WAS EVIDENCE OF A STRUGGLE BEFORE HE FELL FROM THE TOP OF THE PRECIPICE!

Panel 6: THIS WHOLESALE MURDER CANNOT CONTINUE! FIRST EL FIDELDO, THEN DOSSER, THEN TOFFY TEETH...

BUD NEILL

Panel 7: BUT THERE IS NO TRACE OF BAJIN, CAPTAIN ... I HAVE LOOKED EVERY-WHERE!

I'VE GOT IT! THE BLOOD-HOUND!

23₂

Panel 8: LATER...

HERE, ROVER- TAKE A GOOD SNIFF AT THIS GUN OF BAJIN'S THEN SCRAM AFTER HIM LIKE A CLEVER DOGGIE, PLEASE...

YAP YAP

ON THE RAILROAD: CREEPING UP BEHIND RANK BAJIN IS RID SKWERR

WITH DOSSER OUT OF THE WAY I HAVE NO MORE TO WORRY ABOUT! I WILL HOLD CALTON CREEK IN TERROR... I WILL DESTROY IT... I WILL BLOW IT TO BITS! I AM PRACTICALLY OMNIPOTENT & A MEGALOMANIAC INTO THE BARGAIN...

WITH A MIGHTY LEAP, RID SKWERR IS ON BAJIN'S BACK...

CURSES! ATTACKED!

HEE-HEE-HEE! PIT YOUR PUNY STRENGTH AGAINST RANK BAJIN, VILLAIN, WOULDST THOU!

233

WHY, YOU MISERABLE LITTLE APOLOGY FOR A TADPOLE... I COULD SQUEEZE THE LIFE OUT OF YOU WITH ONE HAND AND WILL NOW PROCEED TO DO SO...

UGH!

BUD NEILL

LOBEY'S BROTHER, DUNNY, PREPARES for A JOURNEY

WHOEVER KILLT LOBEY HUD BETTER WATCH OOT... I'LL GET HIM IF IT TAKES ME THE REST O' MA LIFE...

BAJIN DONE IT!

BUT HE'S DISAPPEART!

DON'T WORRY- I'LL FIN' HIM SUPPOSE I'VE TAE CHASE HIM TAE CHINA... I'LL AWA' THEN, CHEERIO!

CHEERIO, DUNNY- AN' GUID LUCK!

TA TA!

BUD NEILL

LATER, ON THE RAILROAD...

IT'S ROON' ABOOT HERE THEY BURRIT LOBEY... WHIT'S THAT ON THE LINE?

234

IT'S WEE RID... DEID ...STRANGILT... PUIR WEE THING... I'M COMIN' EFTER YE, BAJIN, YE MURDERIN' DIVIL!

GOOD OLD ROVER! HE HAS SNIFFED BAJIN'S GUN AND IS HOT ON THE TRAIL OF THE SCOUNDREL!

SNUFF

ONE HOUR LATER ...

THE BLOODHOUND IS HEADING INTO THE HILLS... HE HAS PICKED UP BAJIN'S SCENT!

ATTA BOY, ROVER!

TWO HOURS LATER ...

HE IS GETTING EXCITED! HE IS NEARING THE QUARRY!

SIC 'IM, ROVER BOY!

235

THREE HOURS LATER ...

OAF!

JOE'S WHINSTONE QUARRY CO., LTD. 'VOTE FOR WHINSTONE NEXT TIME'

YAP YAP

AT BAJIN'S HIDEOUT

BUSINESS IS REMARKABLY GOOD ALTHO' THERE ISN'T THE MONEY ABOUT THAT THERE USED TO BE. I HAVE BUMPED OFF EL FIDELDO, DOSSER T.T., AND LITTLE RID SKWERR ...

I WILL NOW PROCEED TO DO IN THE REST OF THE CHARACTERS - THE CAPTAIN, RUBBER LUGS, AND ANYONE ELSE WHO CROSSES MY PATH. I WILL ... HARK! I HEAR A BLOODHOUND BAYING!

HALF-A-MILE AWAY THE CAPTAIN'S CLEVER HOUND IS HOT ON THE TRAIL ...

ROVER IS BANG ON THE SCENT NOW, ALL RIGHT - HE HAS HIS EYE ON SOMETHING!

GOOD DOGGIE!

236

DOLT!

A BLACK PUDDING!

YAP YAP

SEARCHING for BAJIN, DUNNY DOSSER SEES SMOKE RISING FROM A GULLY...

SOMEBODY CAMPIN'! I'LL SNEAK OWER AN' HAE A LOOK!

I AM VERY PARTIAL TO TOASTED CHEESE, I MUST SAY ...YUM, YUM, YUM...

MEANWHILE, A SHORT DISTANCE FROM THE BAJIN HIDEOUT...

TAKE THAT BLACK PUDDING CHASER HOME, LIEUTENANT! HE IS STRICTLY NO USE ...I AM GOING OVER TO INVESTIGATE THIS SMELL OF BURNING CHEESE...

AYE, AYE, SIR!

237

LATER...

BAJIN AT LAST! AND THERE'S DUNNY, TOO! WE'VE GOT THE ROGUE THIS TIME!

RUBBER LUGS'S POSSE HAS HAD NO LUCK IN THEIR SEARCH FOR THE NOTORIOUS KILLER, RANK BAJIN...

YOU BOYS GO ON HOME —I'LL HAVE A LOOK AROUND ON MY OWN...

OKAY, CHIEF!

LATER...

A DISTINCT AROMA OF WELSH RAREBIT ... I SHALL INVESTIGATE

BAJIN! AND THERE'S DUNNY AND THE CAPTAIN! THE ROGUE HAS NO CHANCE...

238

WELL, I MUST SAY MY TOASTED CHEESE WAS VERY DELICIOUS —AND THESE 3 JERKS WHO ARE WATCHING ME THINK THEY HAVE BEEN UNOBSERVED ...THEY DO NOT KNOW THAT I HAVE X-RAY EYES, THE DOPES... THEY WILL GET SOME SURPRISE IN A MINUTE OR TWO, I CAN TELL YOU!

IN THE LATE SHERIFF'S OFFICE ...

AFTER SUCH BLATANT MUTINY AS I ENCOUNTERED YESTERDAY I HAVE NO OPTION BUT TO GO FORWARD WITH MY EARLIER PLAN OF BLOWING CALTON CREEK TO SMITHEREENS! I HAVE THE SPADE, THE FUSE, AND THE TNT!

THAT NIGHT...

I HAVE BURROWED SUFFICIENTLY FAR ... I WILL IGNITE THE FUSE AND GET OUT OF HERE VERY SMARTLY I CAN TELL YOU... THERE!

FIZZ FIZZ...

LATER, FROM THE HILLS ABOVE THE CREEK, BAJIN SEES THE TOWN DISINTEGRATE IN A BLINDING FLASH OF FLAME...

BOOM

HEE HEE HEE

243

NEXT MORNING...

NOT A LIVING SOUL LEFT! EVERY BUILDING IN RUINS! REVENGE IS SWEET! NOW I WILL GALLOP OFF TO MEXICO AND START MY EVIL LIFE AFRESH ... HEE-HEE-HEE .., HA-HA-HA ... HO-HO-HO!

WELL, IT LOOKS AS THOUGH BAJIN'S THE WEE BOY!

THE EARLY MORNING SUN STREAMS BRIGHTLY THROUGH A CERTAIN CHARACTER'S WINDAE...

?

HIVVENS, WHIT A NIGHTMARE! THAT REAL, TAE! MUST HIV BEEN THAE PICKELT ONIONS AND CHEESE I ETT AFORE I WENT TAE BED ... THAT WIS AWFY. RIGHT ENOUGH!

FELL OOT THE BED AN' A' ... HAUF-PAST-SIX ... TIME I WIS UP AN' WASHED ... THAT REAL, TAE ... YAWN, YAWN

244

HERE, SUPPOSE IT WUS REAL AN' I'M DEID, RIGHTENUFF! BETTER TAKE A LOOK OOTSIDE!

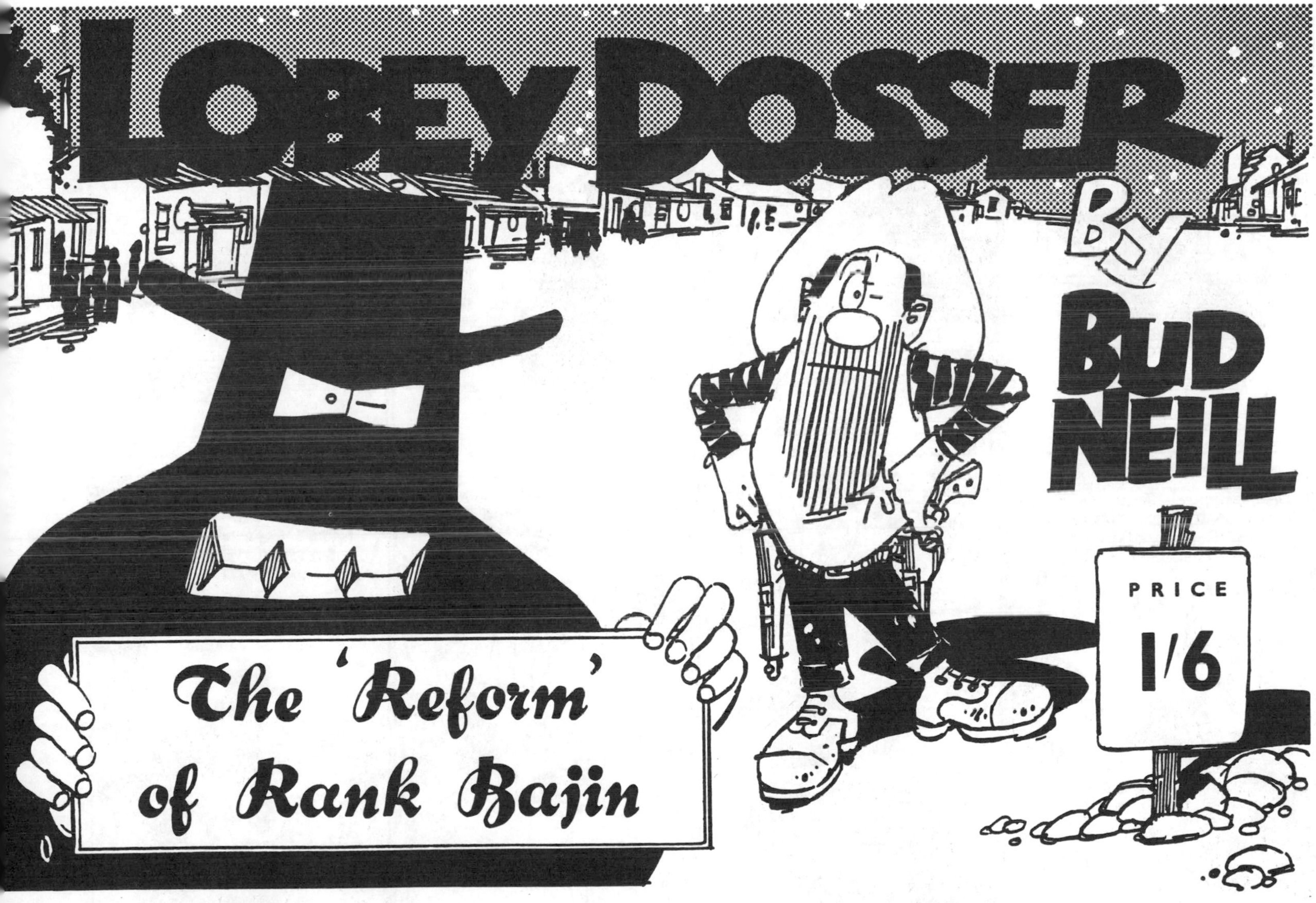

LOBEY DOSSER
By
BUD NEILL
The 'Reform' of Rank Bajin
PRICE
1/6

PERHAPS I MAY PREVAIL UPON MY BROTHER, A.S., TO TAKE OVER DURING MY ABSENCE

IT WOULD BE RERR IF YE COULD, RANKIE

HE'S VERY GOOD AT HOLD-UPS AND PETTY PILFERING...

SOUNDS IDEAL

DOES A LITTLE GRAND LARCENY, TOO, BUT HIS FORTE IS SNATCHING BAGS FROM ELDERLY LADIES... TRAINED IN GLASGOW'S WEST END

JIST THE TICKET

17

SUPPOSE YOU ACCOMPANY ME ON MY VISIT TO HIM, DOSSER?

AYE, SURE! ONY TIME THAT SUITS YE...

MY WINGS IS WABBIT FLEEIN' HERE WITH NEWS THAT AIN'T SO GOOD, I FEAR THE VILLAIN RANK AND LOBEY D. ARE GOING OFF OSTENSIBLY TO VISIT BAJIN'S BROTHER— WELL, A RAT DOES THIS WEE FAIRY SMELL FOR IF SHE KNOWS THE VILLAIN RANKIE HE'S UP TO SOME OLD HANKIE-PANKIE

18

BACK TO THE CREEK WE'LL SMARTLY WALK AND ON THE ROAD WE'LL HAVE A TALK TO THWART RANK BAJIN'S FELONY— OH, DEAR—MY WINGS ARE KILLIN' ME!

CALTON CREEK 1 MILE →